Edgar Allan Poe

AMERICAN HORROR

THREE TERRIFYING TALES

Text adaptation, notes and activities
by **Kenneth Brodey**

D1195919

Somerset County Library
Bridgewater, NJ 08807

Editors: Rebecca Raynes, Frances Evans
Design and art direction: Nadia Maestri
Computer graphics: Simona Corniola
Illustrations: Gianni De Conno
Picture Research: Laura Lagomarsino

New Edition
© 2003   Black Cat Publishing,
            an imprint of Cideb Editrice, Genoa, Canterbury

Every effort has been made to trace copyright holders of material in this
book. Any rights not acknowledged here will be acknowledged in subse-
quent printings if notice is given to the publisher.

All rights reserved. No part of this book may be reproduced, stored in a
retrieval system, or transmitted, in any form or by any means, electronic,
mechanical, photocopying, recording or otherwise, without the written
permission of the publisher.

We would be happy to receive your comments and suggestions, and give
you any other information concerning our material.
editorial@blackcat-cideb.com
www.blackcat-cideb.com
www.cideb.it

CISQ CISQ CERT
TEXTBOOKS AND
TEACHING MATERIALS
The quality of the publisher's
design, production and sales processes has
been certified to the standard of
UNI EN ISO 9001

ISBN 88-530-0020-1   Book
ISBN 88-530-0021-X   Book + CD

Printed in Italy by Litoprint, Genoa

CONTENTS

INTERNET PROJECT : for further information and links for this project visit the student area on our site at www.blackcat-cideb.com

 FCE   First Certificate in English Examination-style exercises

T: GRADE 7   Trinity-style exercises (Grade 7)

This story is recorded in full.

    These symbols indicate the beginning and end of the extracts linked to the listening activities.

Edgar Allan Poe (1845) selfportrait.
Bloomington Indiana University, Lily Library.

Edgar's Life

"From childhood's hour I have not been
As others were — I have not seen
As others saw

And all I loved, I loved alone"
From Edgar's poem "Alone"

Edgar Allan Poe is famous for his tales of horror. He is also considered the inventor of the modern detective story, the modern short story itself and modernist poetry. In addition he was one of the earliest creators of science fiction. His stories were also the basis for that great popular art form, the horror film. More books have been written about Edgar Allan Poe than any other American author. In part, this is because of his great artistic influence, but also because his life was as mysterious and tragic as his stories and poems.

He was born on January 19, 1809 in Boston. His parents were both actors. His mother, who went to the United States in 1796 from England, was a very good actress. Magazines and newspapers wrote good things about her. At the age of 15 she already knew more than 70 different theatrical roles. Edgar's father, on the other hand, was a very bad actor and could not make enough money to support his family. In fact, when Edgar was only two years old his father left the family. Nobody knows where he went.

This is the beginning of Edgar's troubles. [1] Soon after his father left, his mother became very ill with tuberculosis. Nobody helped her. She was only twenty-four years old and had three children. She died on December 8, 1811. Edgar was only two years old.

Fortunately, Mrs Frances Allan, the wife of John Allan, a businessman from Richmond, Virginia, heard about the Poe children. As an act of charity she decided to bring Edgar to live in her house. She was impressed with his good looks. [2] Mrs Allan's husband agreed to have Edgar live in their house, but he refused to officially adopt him. Mr Allan did not want his heir [3] to be the son

---

1. **troubles** [trʌblz] : problems, difficulties.
2. **good looks** : if you have good looks it means you are beautiful/handsome.
3. **heir** [eə(r)] : your heir is the person who you decide will receive your property when you die.

of actors. Acting at this time was considered an immoral profession. Edgar suffered because of this decision, and his relationship with Mr Allan was never good. In 1815 the Allans, together with Edgar, went to live in England for five years. When they returned to the United States in 1820 Edgar went to private schools in Richmond. In 1826 he went to the University of Virginia. He was a very good student, but Mr Allan did not send him enough money to live. In order to make money for school, Edgar gambled. [1] But he was not a good gambler and lost money. John Allan still refused to help him. Edgar had to get a job as a clerk.

In 1827 he published his first book of poems. In this same year he joined the United States Army. In 1829 he went to West Point, the American military academy. In this period, after the death of his wife, John Allan ended forever his relationship with Edgar. In 1832 Edgar went to Baltimore to live with his aunt and his 11-year-old cousin, Virginia Clemm. In 1833 Edgar won a literary contest [2] for his short story

Virginia Clemm Poe (1843)
by Edgar Allan Poe.
Bloomington Indiana University, Lily Library.

1. **gambled** : played games (card games, roulette, etc.) for money.
2. **contest** : competition.

"MS. Found in a Bottle". This is the beginning of Edgar's professional career as a writer.

From 1835 to 1837 he worked as the editor of the literary magazine *Southern Literary Messenger*. He did an extremely good job: sales increased from 500 to 3,500 copies. As editor he explored new areas. He wrote reviews [1] for Latin grammars, dictionaries, other magazines, novels and poetry. He was a fair [2] but very severe critic. He did not care [3] if an author was famous or not. He wrote what he thought.

In 1836, while Edgar was working for the *Southern Literary Messenger*, he married his cousin Virginia Clemm. Like Edgar's mother, she had tuberculosis, and for the next ten years until her death she was constantly ill.

Even with Edgar's success as an editor he did not make enough money to support his family. He therefore moved to New York and then to Philadelphia in 1838 and then back to New York in 1844, always looking for better jobs.

In 1840 he published his greatest tales in a collection called *Tales of the Grotesque and Arabesque*. In 1843 he wrote "The Gold Bug", a kind of treasure hunt story with hidden clues, [4] which sold 300,000 copies. This story brought Poe fame, but not financial security. In fact he often worked 15 hours a day, and still he did not have enough money to feed [5] his family.

In 1845 Edgar's most famous poem, "The Raven", [6] was published.

1. **reviews** [rɪ'vjuːs] : articles that evaluate the quality of something.
2. **fair** : just, honest.
3. **he did not care** : it was not important to him.
4. **clues** : indications that help to solve a mystery or puzzle.
5. **feed** : provide food for (used for people or animals).
6. **Raven** :

He was finally successful. But in 1847 his wife died. This "intolerable sorrow" [1] caused Edgar to drink, and, it seems, he had a very low tolerance for alcohol. He returned to Richmond in 1849.

Edgar's sadness for the death of his wife and his drinking made him ill. On October 3, 1849 Edgar was found unconscious in front of a voting station in Baltimore. He was taken to hospital, where he died four days later.

Edgar's misfortune did not end with his death. The man who controlled his literary works, Rufus Griswold, was very jealous of Edgar's genius. He wrote the official obituary [2] of Edgar in which he spoke very badly of Edgar. Because of this obituary Edgar's reputation was destroyed for many years. In addition, shortly before his death Edgar had revised all his works, but Griswold only published some of them, and often without Edgar's corrections.

Fortunately, though, the great French poet Charles Baudelaire spent 14 years translating Edgar's stories, which then became extremely important for French literature. Then when French literature became important for English literature, Edgar was finally considered as an important writer in England and America.

Rufus Griswold.

1. **sorrow** : sadness.
2. **obituary** : article in a newspaper reporting the death of a person and also telling about that person's life.

Edgar's Horror

Edgar's horror stories, or "arabesques" as he called them, are particular. They are often full of precise, physical details and reasoning. He analyzes the mentality of madmen with the care of a psychologist or of a detective. In "The Black Cat" and "The Tell-Tale Heart" the narrators of these stories analyze their own madness carefully and calmly. But still they can do nothing about it. They remain mad. They commit horrible crimes. This, perhaps, is the most frightening thing about these stories. Also, as Edgar wrote many times, his stories are not about the horrors that exist in the outside world, but the horrors that exist in our own minds. Another reason to be frightened!

Bela Lugosi in a scene of the 1934 film version of *The Black Cat*.

Edgar's Detective Stories

"Murders in the Rue Morgue" (1841) is considered the first detective story. Before this, there had been stories about murders, but before Poe the act of murder itself was the most important part of the story; after Poe, the most important part of the story was the collection of facts and the reasoning about these facts needed to solve the mystery.

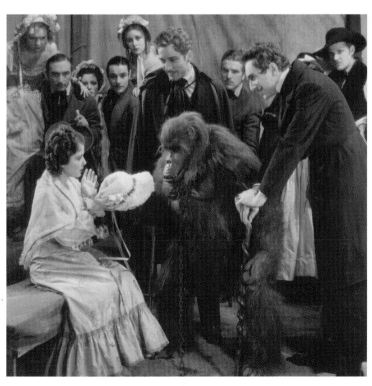

A scene from the 1932 film version of *Murders in the Rue Morgue*, starring Bela Lugosi.

In addition, and just as important for the history of literature, Edgar created the first great character of detective stories, Monsieur C. Auguste Dupin. Dupin is the ancestor of Conan Doyle's Sherlock Holmes, Agatha Christie's Hercule Poirot and Erle Stanley Gardner's Perry Mason (see pages 68-72).

Dupin is also another one of Edgar's mad characters, but a "harmless [1] madman", who reads during the day and goes out only at night; and who, with imagination and reason, is able to solve the crimes committed by others.

Some of Edgar's Most Famous Stories

The Tales of Ratiocination (detective stories)
"The Gold Bug" (1843)
"Murders in the Rue Morgue" (1841)
"The Mystery of Marie Roget" (1842-1843)
"The Purloined Letter" (1844)

Tales of the Grotesque
"Fall of the House of Usher" (1839)
"The Pit and the Pendulum" (1842)
"The Cask of Amontillado" (1846)

---

1. **harmless** : a harmless person, animal, etc., will not hurt (harm) you.

Go back to the text

1 **Here is a summary of what you have just read. Circle the correct answers.**

Edgar was born in Boston on January 19, **a** *(1709 / 1809 / 1909)*. Both his parents were **b** *(bankers / businessmen / actors)*. His father abandoned the family when Edgar was two years old, and his mother died soon after.

After this Edgar went to live with the Allans. But Mr Allan never officially **c** *(liked / admired / adopted)* Edgar.

In 1815 the Allans, together with Edgar, went to live in **d** *(France / Germany / England)* for five years. In 1820 they returned to the United States. In 1826 Edgar attended the University of **e** *(Pennsylvania / Massachusetts / Virginia)*. He was a good student but Mr Allan did not send him enough money, so Edgar had to **f** *(rob banks / steal / gamble)* to make money. Finally, in 1829, Mr Allan ended his relationship with Edgar.

In 1833 Edgar won a **g** *(beauty / literary / boxing)* contest. Three years later he was working as **h** *(editor / writer / composer)* for a literary magazine. He was very successful, but he still did not make enough money.

1n 1836 he married his **i** *(sister / cousin / friend)* Virginia Clemm who was very ill. She died ten years later.

Edgar continued to be successful as an editor and to write many great stories and poems, but his financial problems continued until his death in **j** *(1949 / 1849 / 1749)*.

Edgar became very famous and important in France because the poet **k** *(Charles Baudelaire / Victor Hugo / Charles Rimbaud)* translated all his great stories. Edgar is also famous for having invented the first **l** *(love / detective / horror)* stories. Monsieur C. Auguste Dupin, the hero of these stories, is the literary ancestor of **m** *(Rambo / Sherlock Holmes / David Copperfield)*.

Horror sounds: an audio glossary

2 **Read the definitions below. Then listen to the recording and match the definitions with the sounds.**

a. **to whisper** : to talk softly so that only the person you are talking to can hear you.

b. **to creak** : the sharp sound a door with unoiled hinges makes when you open it.

c. **to cry out** : to say something loudly, or make a loud sharp sound, because you are in pain or frightened.

d. **to cry** : to produce tears (drops of water from your eyes) because you are sad or afraid.

e. **to groan** : to make a low sound because you are in pain or afraid.

f. **to scream** : to make a very loud sharp (acute) sound because you are in pain or frightened: N.B.: to scream is much louder than to cry out.

g. **to shout** : to speak very loudly.

1 ☐   2 ☐   3 ☐   4 ☐   5 ☐   6 ☐   7 ☐

Now practice the sounds with your partner.

A Poe picture gallery

3 **Read the summaries of four famous stories by Edgar Allan Poe, and decide which answer, A, B, C or D, best fits each space. There is an example at the beginning.**
Then match the summaries with the titles given below, and write the correct title under the right pictures on the following pages.

The Masque of the Red Death
The Unparalleled Adventures of One Hans Pfaall
The Pit and the Pendulum
Murders in the Rue Morgue

a. A man is sentenced to death (0) ...A.... slow torture. He is tied down in a small room where there is a (1) .... deep hole and overhead there is a (2) .... of knife attached (3) .... a rope that is moving back and forth like the pendulum of a clock: Each time it goes back and forth it comes closer to the man (4) .... it is almost touching him. The terror, of course, is extreme!

b. A young man from Rotterdam has (5) .... debts. He escapes in a horse of air. But where? To the moon of course! He (6) .... his story with exact scientific details, which in part inspired the future father of science fiction, Jules Verne. (*Journey to the Center of the Earth, Around the World in Eighty Days*).

c. This story, (7) .... takes place in Paris, is often (8) .... the first detective story, and its hero, Monsieur C. August Dupin, the first literary detective. There are very strange murders in this story. The victims are killed by someone with superhuman strength. Different people hear the murderer talking in a "foreign" language. Whodunit?

d. This is the story of a prince who tries to escape death. The prince's kingdom is being destroyed by the plague, that terrible disease which periodically decimated Europe (9) .... the Middle Ages. The symbol and sign of the Plague is the red of blood, and no one can escape it, but the prince tries. He takes all his ladies and knights into his castle where he has luxurious parties, (10) .... everyone outside is dying. Will death be an unexpected and unwanted guest at the prince's party?

0. **A** by **B** for **C** of **D** from
1. **A** much **B** such **C** so **D** very
2. **A** brand **B** kind **C** species **D** class
3. **A** from **B** to **C** by **D** on
4. **A** since **B** while **C** until **D** when
5. **A** many **B** much **C** plenty **D** lots
6. **A** says **B** speaks **C** talks **D** tells
7. **A** which **B** who **C** that **D** those
8. **A** thought **B** considered **C** believed **D** regarded
9. **A** during **B** through **C** for **D** in
10. **A** when **B** until **C** as **D** while

1 [ ] ....

2 [ ] ....

3 [ ] ....

4 [ ] ....

THE BLACK CAT

Before reading

1 **Match the names of the animals with their definitions.**
Then tick the animals which are generally kept as pets.

1. ☐ dog   2. ☐ bat
3. ☐ rabbit   4. ☐ cheetah
5. ☐ bird   6. ☐ hedgehog
7. ☐ fox   8. ☐ goldfish
9. ☐ trout   10. ☐ monkey

a. ☐ A freshwater fish related to salmon which is good to eat.

b. ☐ A medium-sized member of the order of primates – the order which includes human beings, gorillas, lemurs and chimpanzees. They generally live in tropical countries and eat fruit and leaves.

c. ☐ A small mouse-like animal with wings that is active at night. It hangs upside down when it is resting.

d. ☐ A small orange-red fish, originally from eastern Asia, which is kept in bowls and ponds.

e. ☐ A small furry mammal with long ears, a short tail and long back legs used for jumping.

f. ☐ A carnivorous animal with ears, a furry tail and a muzzle. The adults of this animal range considerably in size: the smallest can weigh as little as 4 kilos and the largest can weigh as much as 65 kilos. Its typical call is a bark.

g. ☐ A warm-blooded animal with two legs, wings and feathers that lays eggs.

h. ☐ A medium-sized carnivorous animal with pointed ears, a long furry tail and a long muzzle. It has a reddish brown coat and is known for its exceptional intelligence.

i. ☐ This is a large African animal with a yellowish-brown coat with black spots. It is the fastest land animal in the world and can reach speeds up to 110 km/h.

j. ☐ A small animal with a pointed head and spines on its back. When attacked it rolls itself up into a ball to protect itself.

Before going on

2 The spirit of the perverse
Do you ever do what *you know* you shouldn't do? Discuss with your partner if you ever:

- say nasty things to your friend or someone you love
- don't tell the truth for no good reason at all
- don't do your homework when you have plenty of time
- break something valuable
- eat the last pastry, candy, cake, etc. when you know somebody else hasn't eaten yet
- don't go to bed when you should, even if you are tired
- drive your bike or motorcycle too fast
- Other

3 **Listen to the first chapter of "The Black Cat" and decide whether the statements are true (T) or false (F).**

		T	F
a.	The narrator is going to die tomorrow.	☐	☐
b.	When the narrator was a child, he hated animals.	☐	☐
c.	He had a large white cat.	☐	☐
d.	His cat's name was Pluto.	☐	☐
e.	He became a victim of alcohol.	☐	☐
f.	He cut off his cat's head.	☐	☐
g.	He was not sorry for what he had done to his cat.	☐	☐
h.	He killed Pluto because he knew that his cat loved him.	☐	☐

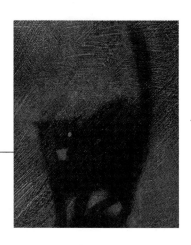

Chapter One

do not think people will believe my story. But I am not mad, and I am not dreaming. Tomorrow I will die and I want to make a confession. The events which I am going to describe here have terrified me, have tortured me, have destroyed me. To me they seemed horrible and supernatural, but perhaps somebody who is calmer and more rational will find a logical explanation. This is my story.

I was a very kind and gentle [1] child who loved animals. As I grew up this love for animals became greater. This is easy to understand: it is difficult to trust [2] people, but you can always trust a faithful dog.

---

1. **gentle** : not violent.
2. **trust** : if you trust someone, you are sure they are good, you are sure they will not hurt you.

I married when I was young and my wife liked animals too. We had birds, gold-fish, a dog, rabbits, a small monkey, and a *cat*. This cat was quite large, beautiful, completely black and extremely intelligent. In fact, my wife sometimes said that our cat was probably a witch [1] in disguise. [2] She was not really *serious* about this, and I mention it now only because by chance [3] I remember it. Pluto — this was the cat's name — was my favorite pet and playmate. [4] He followed me everywhere.

Unfortunately, I became a victim of alcohol. I drank more and more. Of course, my personality changed. I became moody [5] and irritable with my wife and pets. At the beginning, though, I respected Pluto and never hurt him. But one night I returned home very intoxicated. [6] I thought that Pluto was avoiding me. I held him violently and in his fright the cat bit my hand. I became furious. I was possessed by a demon. I caught the cat again. Then I took a pocket-knife from my pocket, opened it and cut out his eye! I blush, [7] I burn while I now write these facts. The next day I felt horror for my action, but I continued to drink, and wine made me forget the horrible thing I had done.

1. **witch :**

2. **in disguise** [dɪsqaɪz] : with its real identity hidden; it was a witch in the form of a cat.
3. **by chance** : accidentally.
4. **playmate** : my companion in play, the friend I always played with.
5. **moody** : moody means that one minute you are happy and one minute you are angry.
6. **intoxicated** : drunk, ("drunk" means you have drunk a lot of alcohol).
7. **I blush** : my face becomes red because I am sorry (ashamed) for what I did.

The cat got better. The empty eye socket [1] was frightening, but the cat was no longer in pain. [2] He went about the house as usual, but, obviously, he ran away from me in terror. At first I was sorry about this, but soon it made me angry. And then came the spirit of PERVERSENESS. Philosophy does not talk about this spirit, but it is a fundamental part of the human heart. We have all done stupid or terrible things simply because we know that we *should not* do them. This, then, is PERVERSENESS.

This spirit of perverseness, I say, destroyed me because one day I decided to kill poor Pluto. With tears in my eyes and sadness in my heart I put a noose [3] around his neck and hanged him from a tree. I hanged Pluto only because I knew he loved me, only because he had never hurt me, only because I knew that God would never pardon me for the crime.

---

1. **socket** : hole, place in the head where the eye is.
2. **was no longer in pain** : stopped being in pain (**no longer** : not any more).

3. **noose** :

Go back to the text

1 Match the first part of the sentences in column A with the second part in column B.

A

1. His wife thought that Pluto was a witch
2. He loved animals more than people
3. The narrator became moody and irritable
4. Pluto ran away from him in terror
5. We all do stupid or terrible things
6. He killed Pluto

B

a. because we know that we shouldn't do them.
b. because it is easier to trust animals.
c. because he had cut out his eye with a pen-knife.
d. because he knew that Pluto loved him.
e. because he drank too much.
f. because he was black and very intelligent.

2 They go together like love and marriage
Below is a list of words you read in Chapter One. Put them in the correct column of the chart.

> bit   liked   logical   irritable   drank   hurt   ran away
> tortured   hanged   witch   terrified   calmer   furious
> playmate   trust   kind   mad   married   terror   demon
> intelligent   destroy   gentle   dreaming   noose   understand
> personality   frightening   drink   wine   spirit   die   heart
> philosophy   possessed   horror   angry

intoxicated	love	pain	kill

supernatural	rational	moody	fright

T: GRADE 7

3 **Theme – Giving Advice and Opinions**
At what age should young people be able to:

Drink alcohol

Go to a night club

Stay out until 2am

Smoke cigarettes

Leave school and get a job

Drive a car

Imagine a young brother/sister wants to do all the things mentioned at the age of 14, what would you advise him/her?

25

We have all done stupid things

When we wish to talk about a period of time that began in the past
and continues up to the present we use the Present Perfect.
Often the period of time we are referring to is a person's life,
especially when we use the adverb "ever" in the question.
Look at the following examples:
- *Have you ever done anything stupid?*
- *Yes, I have done many stupid things.*
- *Have they ever traveled by plane?*
- *Yes, they have.*

Now look at the following short dialogues and notice that the Past
Simple is used when we begin to ask or talk about something specific
in the past.
- *Have you ever lost your wallet?*
  Yes, I have.
- *When did you lose your wallet?*
  I lost it during my summer holiday last summer.
- *Have you ever studied American literature?*
  Yes, I have.
- *When did you study it?*
  I studied it when I was a high school student.

4 Use the elements below to ask the narrator of the story questions, and
then give his answers according to what you have read. You must
decide if the verbs should be in the Present Perfect or the Past Simple
tenses. If the question is in the Present Perfect use the adverb "ever".

a.	You: have/a dog?	*Have you ever had a dog?*
b.	Narrator	*Yes, I have.*
c.	enjoy/walking/a dog?	*Did you enjoy walking it?*
d.	Narrator	....
e.	have/a cat?	....
f.	Narrator	....
g.	what/be/its name?	....
h.	Narrator	....
i.	what/be like?	....

j. Narrator ....

k. you/be/violent? ....

l. Narrator ....

m. why/you/violent? ....

n. Narrator ....

o. you/do/something ....

you knew was wrong? ....

p. Narrator ....

q. what/you/do? ....

r. Narrator ....

s. why/you/do/it? ....

t. Narrator ....

5 **Find the 21 Past Participles in the verb square which are all in the previous chapter, circle them like the example.**

B	E	C	O	M	E	A	S	G	E	F	G
G	F	O	I	T	H	O	U	G	H	T	E
H	O	M	M	B	A	C	O	M	E	N	T
D	A	N	S	I	D	F	A	T	A	Y	H
T	H	N	E	T	H	C	E	M	O	D	E
C	H	E	G	T	E	A	S	L	M	M	E
P	U	T	H	E	L	U	T	G	T	S	A
Y	T	T	S	N	D	G	A	O	O	F	S
A	H	U	R	T	D	H	K	T	O	I	A
S	D	Y	K	L	M	T	E	R	K	D	I
A	S	D	R	U	N	K	N	O	W	N	D
G	R	O	W	N	U	P	Z	E	E	R	G

6 Now complete each of the following sentences using the Past Simple of the appropriate irregular verb.

Example: He **hurt** Pluto for no good reason.

a. The more I drank, the more I .... irritable and moody.

b. My wife .... that Pluto was a witch in disguise.

c. My wife and I .... lots of pets.

d. When he was a boy he loved animals, but when he .... he loved them even more.

e. The cat tried to escape, but he .... it.

f. The dog looked friendly, but when I tried to caress it, it .... me.

Things we should not do

Look at this:
You should help your friends.
= It would be a good idea if you helped your friends.
You shouldn't steal. = It is not a good idea to steal.

7 Using the verbs in the box to help you, write sentences according to the example.

> **turn on   turn off   steal   eat   ~~tell~~**
> **blow over   clean   open   drive**

Example:

John's sister is reading a mystery story. If she knew the ending it would ruin the story for her. John has read the book before.

John knows he shouldn't tell her the ending but he is going to tell her anyway.

a. Edgar is riding down the highway in his new sports car. It is late at night and no one is around. Now he is going at 100 kilometres per hour, but his car can go much faster.

Edgar ....

b. My sister has spent an hour building a house of playing cards. Any movement of air, and it will fall over. Her little brother is watching her enviously.

Her little brother ....

c. My father worked until late last night. It is eleven in the morning now and I would like to hear some rock music on the radio.

I ....

d. Dominique is in the dark room developing some very important photographs. Charles is in front of the dark room door. If any light enters the room all the photos will be ruined.

Charles ....

e. I can see the box of money on the table, and nobody is in the room. The money was collected for the local hospital.

I ....

f. Thomas sees a piece of chocolate cake on the table. He knows that it is for his sister who loves chocolate cake.

Thomas ....

g. My hands are covered with chocolate and sugar. Juliette's new cashmere sweater is on the chair. I hate having sticky hands.

I ....

h. My sister has just seen a horror film and she is terrified. She is in her bedroom with the light on but the light switch is outside her room!

I ....

Before you go on

 **1 Listen to the beginning of Chapter Two, and complete the following sentences with a word or a short phrase.**

1. The night of the crime there was ....

2. He, his wife and his servant just ....

3. The day after the fire he went to visit ....

4. The people looking at the wall said things like ....
   ....

5. On the wall he saw the figure of a ....

6. He thought that someone had thrown the cat into his bedroom window in order ....

7. The image of the cat was probably made by the ....
   ....

8. The black cat in the bar was almost identical to Pluto except that it had ....

9. When he left the bar, the cat ....

Chapter Two

he night of this crime there was a fire in my house. My wife, my servant and I just managed to escape.[1] My entire wealth [2] was destroyed in the fire and I lost all hope. I do not want to say that there is a connection between my crime and the fire. I only want to record [3] the facts of my story.

The day after the fire I went to visit the ruins of my house. Only one wall remained, and around this wall was a group of people. They were saying things like "strange!", "singular!". I went closer and saw a strange bas-relief on the wall, the figure of a gigantic *cat*. The image was extremely accurate. There was a rope [4] about the animal's neck.

1. **just managed to escape** : were able to escape, but with great difficulty.
2. **wealth** [welθ] : all my money and property.
3. **record** [rɪ'kɔːd] : write down.
4. **rope** :

THE BLACK CAT

When I first saw the image of the cat I was terrified, but I thought about it and found a good explanation. I had hung the cat in the garden next to my house. When the fire began, this garden filled up with people. Somebody probably threw the cat into my bedroom window in order to wake me. The other walls of the house fell in and pressed the body of the cat against this wall. The great heat of the fire and a chemical reaction then made the image.

Although I had a logical explanation, that bas-relief made a great impression on my imagination. For months I could not escape the phantasm of the cat. I even tried to find another cat to substitute it. Then, one night in a bar, I saw a black object on top of some hogsheads [1] of rum. I looked closer. It was a large black cat. It was almost identical to Pluto except it had an indistinct white area on its breast. [2] I caressed the cat and it immediately got up and purred. [3] It was happy. This was the animal I was looking for. I asked the bartender [4] if I could buy it. He said that it was not his. I continued to caress the cat and when I left the bar, the cat followed me home.

END

My wife liked this cat very much. But I began to dislike it. I had thought that I would be happier with a new cat. Instead, the affection of the cat only disgusted me. And slowly this disgust became hatred. I avoided it because I felt some shame [5] for killing Pluto and I did not want to hurt it too. In addition, this cat, just like Pluto, had only one eye.

1. **hogsheads** : barrels.
2. **breast** [brest] : the top front part of the body between the neck and the stomach.
3. **purred** : a cat purrs (makes a sound like a little motor) when it is happy.
4. **bartender** : the person who serves drinks in a bar.
5. **I felt some shame** : I felt a little sorry.

However, the more I hated this cat, the more it followed me. It is difficult to explain how terrible this was. When I sat down it would jump on my legs and cover me with horrible caresses. When I got up to walk it was between my legs and I would almost fall. This made me so angry that I wanted to kill it, but I was stopped — not by the memory of my first crime — but by absolute dread [1] of the beast.

This dread was not exactly a dread of physical evil, [2] but I do not know how to define it. I am almost ashamed [3] to admit — as I wait here in my prison cell — that my terror was caused by something incredibly insubstantial. My wife had often talked about the indistinct white patch [4] on the cat's breast, the only difference between him and Pluto. But this indistinct white patch gradually became distinct. I tried to ignore what I saw. I said to myself that it was just my imagination. But this distinct image was the real reason why I did not dare [5] hurt the beast. It was an image that I feared. It was the image of the GALLOWS! [6] That terrible instrument of Horror and of Crime — of Agony and of Death!

---

1. **dread** [dred] : fear.
2. **evil** [i:vl] : evil is something that is very, very bad.
3. **ashamed** : embarrassed.
4. **patch** : spot, area.
5. **I did not dare** : I did not have the courage.
6. **gallows** :

Go back to the text

FCE **1** **Read the summary of Chapter Two and decide which answer A, B, C or D best fits each space. There is an example at the beginning.**

He did not want to kill Pluto, but he killed him (0) ...A.... , and the night after he killed Pluto his house (1) .... on fire. The fire destroyed his entire wealth and he lost all his hope. The (2) .... day there was a group of people around the ruins of his house, (3) .... were saying things (4) .... as "strange!" and "singular!". Only one wall of his house remained (5) .... on that wall was a strange image: a gigantic cat with a rope around its neck. (6) .... though, he had a logical explanation for this image, it (7) .... a great impression on him.

Still, he (8) .... on drinking and one night in a bar he saw a black object on (9) .... hogsheads of rum. (10) .... was a black cat. He asked the bartender if the cat was his, but it seemed the cat did not (11) .... to anyone. He caressed the cat and the cat followed him home. It was exactly like Pluto (12) .... it had a strange white area on its breast.

Soon, however, he began to hate it. At the same time, he began to avoid it because the white area turned into the image of the gallows.

0. **A** anyway	**B** still	**C** also	**D** even
1. **A** took	**B** made	**C** caught	**D** went
2. **A** after	**B** then	**C** next	**D** near
3. **A** who	**B** which	**C** that	**D** whose
4. **A** similar	**B** like	**C** such	**D** almost
5. **A** but	**B** although	**C** and	**D** or
6. **A** however	**B** also	**C** if	**D** even
7. **A** did	**B** made	**C** forced	**D** created
8. **A** continued	**B** took	**C** maintained	**D** kept
9. **A** some	**B** any	**C** the	**D** those
10. **A** that	**B** this	**C** he	**D** it
11. **A** belong	**B** own	**C** possess	**D** have
12. **A** though	**B** but	**C** except	**D** even

FCE **2** **Choose the correct answer, A, B, C or D.**

1. Why does the narrator mention the story of the fire.

   A ☐ Because he wants people to know that he has suffered greatly, and that his great suffering made him do horrible things.

   B ☐ Because he sees the fire as a sign of divine punishment for his horrible crime.

   C ☐ Because he was sure that the phantasm of Pluto caused the fire.

   D ☐ Because he wants to tell his story honestly and correctly.

2. In the narrator's opinion, how did the image of the cat with a rope around its neck appear on the wall?

   A ☐ A wall of the house fell against the dead cat, which a neighbor had thrown into his bedroom, and the heat of the fire caused a chemical reaction that formed the image.

   B ☐ A neighbor, who wanted to wake him up because of the fire, tried to throw the cat into his bedroom, but the cat hit a wall of the house. Then since the fire had made the wall soft, the cat left its image on the wall.

   C ☐ During the fire a neighbor, who knew that he had killed the cat, made the bas-relief on the wall to frighten him.

   D ☐ The phantasm of the black cat produced the image with magic in order to frighten him.

3. Why did the narrator first begin to avoid the cat?

   A ☐ Because the cat often tried to bite him.

   B ☐ Because he hated it.

   C ☐ Because he thought it was really the phantasm of Pluto.

   D ☐ Because he did not want to kill it.

Although I had a logical explanation

Example:

- *That bas-relief made a great impression on my imagination, **although** I had a logical explanation.*

or

- ***Although** I had a logical explanation, that bas-relief made a great impression on my imagination.*
- *When I first saw the image of the cat I was terrified, **but** I thought about it and found a good explanation.*

3 **Fill in the blanks with either** *although* **or** *but* **according to the context.**

a. I killed Pluto, ... I loved him very much.

b. I knew drinking was bad for me, ... I drank anyway.

c. Edgar Allan Poe wrote many popular stories and poems, ... he still died poor.

d. .... I have read this sentence many times, I still don't understand it.

e. I know that "The Black Cat" is only a story, ... it still frightens me.

f. He ate the last piece of cake, ... he knew that I wanted it.

Before reading

1 **Listen carefully!**

Below are four paragraphs from the last chapter of the story. They are not in the right order. Listen to the recording once and then number them in the right order. Then listen to the recording again and circle the right word to fill in the blanks.

a. ☐ One *(morning / night / day)* we had to go down into the cellar. The cat went between my legs. I almost fell. I *(became / got / was)* furious. I grabbed an axe and tried to *(hit / kill / hurt)* the animal, but my wife blocked my arm. This made me even more furious and I lifted the axe again and buried it in her *(brain / head / heart)*. She fell dead immediately, without a groan.

b. ☐ Oh how I suffered! You cannot imagine. I had *(killed / hurt / destroyed)* a brute beast, and now another brute beast was destroying me. Day or night I could not *(sleep / work / rest)*. During the day the creature never left *(me / us / her)* alone, and at night I woke up hourly from terrible *(images / dreams / nightmares)* with that thing on my *(stomach / face / legs)*. It was a living nightmare always there in my heart.

c. ☐ I had murdered her. Now I had to eliminate the *(corpse / body / cadaver)*. There were many possibilities. I could cut the body into little pieces and then burn them, or I could bury it.

d. ☐ All my good thoughts had gone. *(Evil / Dreadful / Hateful)* thoughts filled my brain. I began to *(dread / dislike / hate)* all things and all mankind. My wife, I am sorry to say, suffered the most.

Now read the chapter and check your answers.

37

Chapter Three

O h how I suffered! You cannot imagine. I had killed a brute beast, and now another brute beast was destroying me. Day or night I could not rest. During the day the creature never left me alone, and at night I woke up hourly from terrible dreams with that thing on my face. It was a living nightmare always there in my heart.

All my good thoughts had gone. Evil thoughts filled my brain. I began to hate all things and all mankind. [1] My wife, I am sorry to say, suffered the most.

One day we had to go down into the cellar. [2] The cat went between my legs. I almost fell. I became furious. I grabbed [3] an

---

1. **mankind** : humanity.
2. **cellar** : the room underground, under the house.
3. **grabbed** : took quickly and with force.

axe [1] and tried to kill the animal, but my wife blocked my arm. This made me even more furious and I lifted the axe again and buried it [2] in her brain. She fell dead immediately, without a groan. [3]

I had murdered her. Now I had to eliminate the body. There were many possibilities. I could cut the body into little pieces and then burn them, or I could bury it.

END

Finally, I decided to put it inside the wall of the cellar. There was a projection in the wall. I pulled out the bricks [4] with a crowbar. [5] I put the body in there and then I carefully put back the bricks. Nobody could see the difference. It was perfect.

Then I went to look for the cat to kill it too. But the beast had escaped. I did not see it that night. I was finally free of its torment and that night I slept tranquilly, even if I had just killed my wife.

The second and the third day passed. The monster did not return. My happiness was supreme. The police came and searched the house, [6] but, of course, they found nothing. I would be happy forever!

Then on the fourth day the police came again. They told me to come with them while they searched the house. They went down into the cellar again and found nothing. I was so happy that I wanted to say something. I wanted to show that I was really not guilty. [7]

1. **axe** :
2. **buried** [berid] **it** : put it inside.
3. **groan** : a low, sad sound you make when you are in pain (Ooooo!).
4. **bricks** :
5. **crowbar** :
6. **searched the house** : looked around the house for evidence of a crime.
7. **guilty** : opposite of innocent.

"Gentlemen," I finally said, "I am glad [1] that you have no more suspicions. Oh, by the bye, [2] isn't this a well constructed house. (Now I can't really remember what I said.) In fact, I think it's an excellently well constructed house. These walls — are you going, gentlemen? — are really solid."

Then in that moment I hit the walls with my cane. [3]

May God protect me! The noise of my cane was answered by a voice from the tomb! At first, the voice was difficult to hear. It was like a child crying. Then it became louder and louder. One long, loud, and continuous scream, completely inhuman that came directly from hell!

For a moment the police and I did not move. But then they easily opened the wall. There inside was the standing corpse, already greatly decayed [4] and covered with blood. On the corpse's head, with its red mouth open and one eye, was the beast, the beast that had made me murder my wife. And now that monster had given me to the hangman. [5] I had walled the monster up within the tomb!

1. **glad** : happy.
2. **by the bye** : by the way, incidentally.
3. **cane** : stick used for walking.
4. **decayed** : decomposed.
5. **hangman** : the man who will hang him with a noose.

Go back to the text

1 **Answer the following questions.**

 a. Why did the narrator kill his wife?

 b. Where did he put the corpse?

 c. Why did the narrator tell the policemen that the house was well constructed?

 d. What did the narrator do to show the policemen that the walls of the house were solidly built?

 e. Why did the cat began to scream?

They told me to come with them

Look at this sentence

verb + object + infinitive

They wanted me to come with them.

Many verbs in English take this construction.

- *They ordered the soldiers to attack.*
- *He told me to go home.*
- *I expect you to be here at nine.* = I think you should be here at nine.
  = I think it is your responsibility to be here at nine.
- *She reminded me to change the light bulb.*
- *The doctor advised me to stop smoking.*
  = The doctor said that it would be a good idea if I stopped smoking.
- *My father taught me how to ride a bicycle.*
- *The teacher lets them use a calculator.*
  = The teachers permits them to use a calculator.
- *They begged us to help them.* = They implored us to help them.
- *I would like you to cook dinner.*
- *Herbert showed me how to bake a carrot cake.*
- *They helped me to repair the car.*

FCE 2 For questions 1-10, complete the second sentence so that it has a similar meaning to the first, using the word given. Do not change the word given. You must use between two and five words, including the word given. Here is an example (0).

0. The policeman forced me to open the door.

MADE

The policeman *made me open* the door.

1. My teacher thinks it is my responsibility to learn all the irregular verbs.

EXPECTS

My teacher .... the irregular verbs.

2. "Clean all the bathrooms!" shouted the sergeant to his men.

ORDERED

The sergeant .... all the bathrooms.

3. Susan gave me directions to her house.

HOW

Susan .... to her house.

4. My mechanic says that it would be a good idea if I bought a new car.

ADVISES

My mechanic .... a new car.

5. My friends always permit me to stay in their apartment.

LET

My friends .... in their apartment.

6. That film caused me to cry.

MADE

That film .... cry.

7. "Don't forget to take your keys," she said to me.

REMINDED

She .... keys.

8. "Please lend me some money, Ahmed," said Harriet.

   BEGGED

   Harriet .... her some money.

9. They gave me a hand cleaning up the house.

   HELPED

   They .... the house.

10. "Bring me another glass of juice," said my friend.

    TOLD

    My friend .... another glass of juice.

11. I learnt how to cook from my mother.

    TAUGHT

    My mother .... to cook.

12. "Will you vote for me?" he said to them.

    WANTED

    He .... for him.

T: GRADE 7

3 Theme – Expressing possibility and uncertainty
"...the beast, the beast that had made me murder my wife."
Think about this statement with your class. Answer the following questions:

a. Do you think it is possible for a ghost or spirit to make people do things they don't want to do? Why, why not?

b. If you saw a ghost, how could you be certain people believed your story?

c. How possible is it that you will see a ghost in your lifetime?

d. What happens to pets when they die in your country?

44

4 Here is a summary of "The Black Cat", but four paragraphs have been removed. Choose the most suitable paragraph from the list A-E. There is one paragraph which you do not have to use.

1

Unfortunately, he began to drink. Of course, drinking made him moody and irritable. One night he was possessed by a demon, as he said, and he grabbed Pluto and cut out one of its eyes. Another night he hung the cat from a tree in the garden.

2

Still, he did not stop drinking and one evening he saw another black cat that resembled Pluto. This cat followed him home. This cat never left him alone. He began to hate this cat too. It became a living nightmare for him, and he began to hate everything and everybody.

3

He then walled up his wife in the cellar. That night he slept peacefully. He also felt better because he thought that the cat had run away forever. When the police came and searched his house they found nothing and left.

4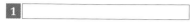

A   After having committed this horrible crime, there was a fire in his house and all his wealth and possessions were destroyed. The next day he went to see the remains of his house. He saw that only one wall was standing, and around this wall there was a crowd of people. They were saying things like "strange!" and "singular!" He came closer and saw a large bas-relief of the cat on the wall!

B The police came several times but they could not find anything. He was very happy about this, but one day he hit the wall of the cellar with his cane and he heard an inhuman screaming which got louder and louder. The police ran to his house and ordered him to open the door.

C One day, while he was going down into the cellar with his wife, this cat almost made him fall. He became furious and grabbed an axe. His wife blocked his arm. This made him even more furious, and he killed her instead.

D They came back a second time. This time he felt very sure of himself because he was certain that the police would never find the corpse. He even hit the wall of the cellar with a cane. But when he did this, he heard an inhuman screaming. The police quickly opened the wall and found the wife's decayed corpse with the cat on her head.

E This story is told by a man in prison. He tells us briefly the story of his life and why he is in prison. When he was a child he was very gentle and loved animals. Later when he got married this love continued and he and his wife had many pets: birds, goldfish, a dog, rabbits and a monkey. They also had a black cat whose name was Pluto. It was very intelligent and his wife sometimes said that it was a witch in disguise.

THE OVAL PORTRAIT

Before reading

1 **What kind of paintings do you like?**

- ☐ Paintings with beautiful, bright colors.
- ☐ Portraits of interesting looking people.
- ☐ Landscapes.
- ☐ Modern paintings.
- ☐ Renaissance paintings.
- ☐ Impressionist paintings.
- ☐ Paintings that are lifelike.
- ☐ Other.

2 **Parts of the human body: outside**
Fill in the chart with the words below.

> thigh   thumb   calf   navel   cheeks   knee   shin
> neck   elbow   wrist   lips   chin   shoulder   ankle
> sole   palm   heel   forearm

head	
trunk	
legs	
feet	
hands	fingers
arms	
between arms/trunk	
between foot/leg	
between head/trunk	neck
between hand/arm	

48

Read the text below and think of the word which best fits each space. Use only one word in each space. There is an example at the beginning (0).

My valet Pedro and I (0) *were* traveling through the Apennine Mountains (1) .... Italy. I was badly hurt and (2) .... a high fever. We finally saw a very strange and gloomy castle that (3) .... been recently abandoned. (4) .... was the kind of castle you can read about (5) .... certain old novels about ghosts. Pedro knew (6) .... I couldn't remain outside in my condition, (7) .... he decided to break into the castle.

(8) .... he had broken in, he took me to a small room in a turret of the castle. This room had many (9) .... old paintings, tapestries and arms. There were also many spirited modern paintings. I looked closely at (10) .... all. They fascinated me greatly, perhaps (11) .... I was delirious from the fever. I also found a book that told the story of (12) .... of the paintings in the room.

Pedro lit the candles of a large candelabrum and I began to contemplate each piece of art in this bizarre room. I lay in my bed reading and looking at the paintings for a long time. Then, (13) .... Pedro was asleep, I moved the candelabrum so I could read (14) .... easily.

 Now listen to the first part of the chapter and check your answer.

THE OVAL PORTRAIT

Chapter One

My valet [1] Pedro and I were traveling through the Apennine Mountains in Italy. I was badly hurt and had a high fever. [2] We finally saw a very strange and gloomy [3] castle that had been recently abandoned. It was the kind of castle that you can read about in certain old novels about ghosts. Pedro knew that I couldn't remain outside in my condition, so he decided to break into [4] the castle.

1. **valet** : servant.
2. **fever** : when your temperature is high because you are ill.
3. **gloomy** : dark, depressing.
4. **to break into** : to enter with force.

When he had broken in, he took me to a small room in a turret of the castle. This room had many very old paintings, tapestries [1] and arms. [2] There were also many spirited [3] modern paintings. I looked closely at them all. They fascinated me greatly, perhaps because I was delirious from the fever. I also found a book that told the story of each of the paintings in the room.

Pedro lit the candles of a large candelabrum and I began to contemplate each piece of art in this bizarre room. I lay [4] in my bed reading and looking at the paintings for a long, long time. Then, since Pedro was asleep, I moved the candelabrum so I could read more easily.

The light of the candles made it easier to read, but it also illuminated a strange little painting in a dark niche. [5] It was the portrait [6] of a lovely adolescent girl. I do not know why, but I closed my eyes for a moment and thought about it.

Then I opened my eyes to look at it again. Then I wondered [7] why I was so charmed [8] by this painting. Its frame [9] was oval and

---

1. **tapestries** : pieces of cloth with designs or pictures on it.
2. **arms** : swords, guns, knives, pistols, etc.
3. **spirited** : lively, vivacious, entertaining, fun.
4. **lay** (lie, lay, lain) : I was resting horizontally.
5. **niche** [ni:ʃ] : hollow area in wall for a statue or painting.
6. **portrait** : a picture of a person, usually of the face.
7. **I wondered** : I asked myself.
8. **charmed** : controlled as if by magic.
9. **frame** :

gold. The painting itself was done very well. It showed the head and shoulders of the girl. The girl herself was extremely beautiful.

The painting had even startled me [1] because for a moment it looked like a living person. Still [2] none of these three things could explain the secret of its mysterious effect on me. Then I discovered the reason: the expression on her face was almost perfectly *lifelike*. [3] And this *lifelikeness* had confused me, startled me and filled me with horror.

I immediately looked in the book for the story of this oval portrait, and read the following story.

1. **startled me** : given me an unexpected shock or surprise.
2. **still** : in spite of that.
3. **lifelike** : like life, in other words, the painting looked extremely real.

Go back to the text

FCE **1** **Choose the right answer A, B, C or D.**

1. What did the castle remind the narrator of?

   A ☐ Ancient warriors.

   B ☐ Books about paintings.

   C ☐ Biographies of famous Renaissance artists.

   D ☐ Castles you read about in books about ghosts.

2. Why might the narrator have paid so much attention to the art in the room?

   A ☐ Because all the paintings seemed so real.

   B ☐ Because there was nothing else to look at.

   C ☐ Because he was delirious from the fever.

   D ☐ Because Pedro fell asleep and left him alone.

3. Why did the narrator move the candelabrum?

   A ☐ So that it would not burn the tapestries.

   B ☐ So he could see the small painting of the girl better.

   C ☐ So its light would not wake up Pedro.

   D ☐ So he could read better.

4. What did the narrator do when he first saw the painting of the young girl?

   A ☐ He closed his eyes and thought about it.

   B ☐ He wondered why it charmed him so much.

   C ☐ He read the story of the painting in the book he had found.

   D ☐ He wondered how the painter had made it so lifelike.

5. What was the secret of the painting's effect on the narrator?

   A ☐ It was an incredibly well executed work of art.

   B ☐ The beauty of the girl in the painting.

   C ☐ The lifelikeness of the design.

   D ☐ The lifelikeness of the expression of the girl.

So and because

Look at the two sentences below:

*Pedro knew I couldn't remain outside **so** he broke into the castle.*

*The paintings fascinated me **because** I was delirious.*

Remember:

The conjunction *so* presents the *consequence* or *result* of a situation.

The conjunction *because* presents the *reason* of a situation.

2 **Complete the following sentences with the appropriate sentences in the box, using *so* or *because*.**

Example:

a.   He had a high fever ***because** he was hurt.*

b.   Pedro was very tired ....
....

c.   He moved the lamp himself ....
....

d.   He couldn't read ....
....

e.   He read the story about the girl in the portrait ....
....

f.   He wanted to discover more about the girl in the portrait ....
....

1.   the portrait had startled and charmed him.

2.   he lay down and went to sleep.

3.   he moved the lamp.

4.   he ~~was~~ hurt.

5.   he read about her in the book.

6.   his servant Pedro was asleep.

Before reading

1 Look at the picture of the girl on page 53, and at the picture of her husband, the artist, on page 61. Describe these two people to your partner, and then say what kind of relationship you think they have. Then report briefly to the class what you and your partner said about these two people.

2 How do you think the story will end?

☐ The young wife will kill her husband because he only thinks about his art.

☐ The young wife will soon die, but she will die happily because she knows that her husband will always be able to see her face and think about her.

☐ The artist will fall in love with the portrait, his creation, and then kill the real, living woman, his wife.

☐ Other...

Artistic words

3 Look at the dictionary extracts below. Then answer the two questions and fill in the blanks in the picture on the opposite page using these words.

brush [brʌʃ] *noun* : an instrument made of a stick and rigid hairs of various kinds that is used for cleaning, painting, etc.: *a hairbrush, a toothbrush, a paintbrush, etc.*

canvas [kænvəs] *noun* : **1** A strong, rigid kind of cloth **2** A piece of this cloth used for oil painting.

casel [i:zl] *noun* : a wooden frame used for holding up a painting (often while it is being painted) or a blackboard.

frame [freɪm] *noun* : **1** The solid structure of a building, automobile, bicycle, piece of furniture etc. **2** The hard protecting edge of something such as a window or picture: *a window frame, a picture frame.*

paint [peɪnt] *noun* : a colored liquid substance you put on a surface to add color, decorate or protect.

paint *verb* : **1** to put paint on a surface **2** to make a picture with paint.

paints *noun* : a complete set of all different colors of paint in tubes, bottles, etc.

palette [pælɪt] *noun* : a thin board usually with a hole for the thumb, which the artist holds while painting and on which the artist mixes color.

portrait [pɔːtreɪt] *noun* : a painting, drawing or photograph of a person, often of the face.

pose [pouz] *verb* : to remain in a certain position, often so an artist can paint your picture or make a sculpture etc.

a. ....   b. ....   c. ....

d. ....   e. ....   f. ....

g. What is the woman doing?

....

h. What is the man doing?

....

FCE 4 **Listen to the first part of Chapter Two and choose the best answer A, B or C.**

1. What was the girl in the portrait like?

   A ☐ Very passionate and austere.

   B ☐ Very sad and beautiful.

   C ☐ Very joyous and beautiful.

2. Who was the painter's other "wife"?

   A ☐ His sister.

   B ☐ His Art.

   C ☐ His castle.

3. What was the only thing that the girl hated?

   A ☐ The painter.

   B ☐ His castle.

   C ☐ His Art.

4. What did the painter ask the girl to do?

   A ☐ To be humble and obedient.

   B ☐ To pose for him.

   C ☐ To not hate her rival.

5. What was the room in the turret of the castle like?

   A ☐ It was cold and unhealthy.

   B ☐ It was full of light, which came from the ceiling.

   C ☐ It was large and full of strange, spirited paintings.

THE STORY OF THE GIRL IN THE PORTRAIT

Chapter Two

The girl in the portrait was extremely beautiful and extremely joyous. But it was an evil hour when she married the painter. He was passionate, austere and studious; and he already had a "wife": his Art.

The girl in the portrait was as happy as a fawn, [1] and she loved and cherished [2] all things; she only hated the Art which was her rival. She was only afraid of the palette, easel and brushes that took her husband away.

It was therefore a terrible thing for her when her husband asked her to pose for a painting. But she was very humble and obedient, and she agreed to pose.

---

1. **happy as a fawn** : joyful, lively and vivacious.
2. **cherished** : loved and considered important.

She posed for this portrait in a cold, unhealthy [1] room of a turret of the castle. The only light in the room came from a small window in the ceiling.

END

The artist worked with energy and only thought of his work. He became obsessed with capturing every shade [2] and color of life on his young wife's face.

Since the room where she was sitting was cold and damp, [3] she got [4] more and more ill. Still, her husband did not notice. All he noticed was his painting. He was a wild and moody man, and he was often lost in his own private dream world. Everybody else saw that his wife was getting weaker and weaker. Still, she continued smiling and never complained because she saw that he took such great interest in this painting: he worked day and night to paint the woman who loved him and who was becoming more and more ill for this love.

Some of the people who saw him working said, "This painting is truly marvelous. It is proof of both his power as a painter and of his love for his wife."

When the painter was finishing the portrait, nobody was allowed in the turret because the painter had become so passionate about his work: he rarely took his eyes from the canvas to look at his wife's face.

1. **unhealthy** [ʌnhelθi] : not healthy; something that is unhealthy will make you ill.
2. **shade** : here, small differences in the same basic colour.
3. **damp** : humid.
4. **got** : (here) became.

In fact, he had become so obsessed with his work that he did not notice that as he put red and pink on the canvas, [1] red and pink left his young wife's cheeks.

Finally he only needed to add a little bit of color for the mouth and a little bit of color for the eyes. The living color of his wife's face shone again for a moment and then went out [2] like a lamp.

The painter added the last brushstroke [3] and for one moment was entranced [4] in front of his painting. He then became pale and began to tremble. He then cried loudly, "This is indeed [5] *Life* itself!" Then he looked suddenly at his wife: — *She was dead!*

1. **canvas** : the strong, tight piece of cloth on which a painter paints (see page 56).
2. **went out** : stopped burning or shining (usually of a light or flame).
3. **brushstroke** : the application of paint with one movement (stroke) of the brush.
4. **was entranced** : was filled with great wonder and emotion, as if by magic.
5. **indeed** : certainly, truly, really.

Go back to the text

1 **Answer the following questions.**

   a. Why was the girl afraid of the artist's paintbrushes, paints, easels, canvases and palettes?

     ....

   b. What was the artist like?

     ....

   c. What became the artist's obsession?

     ....

   d. Why did the girl become ill?

     ....

   e. What did everybody else see that the artist himself did not see?

     ....

   f. Why didn't the girl complain?

     ....

   g. What happened as the artist added the last brushstroke to the painting?

     ....

   h. Why did the painter become pale and tremble when he finished his painting?

     ....

T: GRADE **7**

2 **Topic – Youth Culture**
Bring a photo or picture of yourself with your friends or brothers and sisters. Talk about the picture and say:

   a. Who took it and where you were.

   b. What were you and the others wearing and how were you feeling?

   c. How important are pictures and photos to you and young people in general?

   d. Do you like the idea of picture messaging? Why, why not?

He worked day and night to paint the woman who loved him

Look at these sentences:
He painted the woman who loved him.
That is the book which tells the story of the painting.
These are the paintings that fascinated Edgar Allan Poe.
He is the man that told me about Italy.
That is the hotel where we stayed last summer.

They all contain defining relative clauses. A defining relative clause is essential to the sentence: without it the sentence is not complete.

Notice that we use:
- *who* for people
- *which* for animals and things
- *that* for people, animals and things
- *where* for places

In spoken English *that* is generally used instead of *which*.

3 **Answer the questions about the story using a relative clause and the elements below. If a sentence can be made with both *that* and *who*, or *that* and *which* write two different sentences.**

man/break into/castle

~~castle/Pedro and his master/spend the night~~

artist/paint/a strange portrait of his wife

board/painter/use to mix colors

book/tell the story/of the paintings

place/artist painted the strange portrait

girl/die slowly/in the turret

mountains/form/the backbone of central Italy

a man/often traveled in Italy

~~writer/write/"The Oval Portrait"~~

Example: *What is that building?*
   It's the castle where Pedro and his master spent the night.

Example: *Who was Edgar Allan Poe?*
He was the writer who wrote "The Oval Portrait".
He was the writer that wrote "The Oval Portrait".

a. Who is that man with the beard?

b. What did the narrator read?

c. Who was Pedro?

d. Who is that in the painting?

e. What are the Apennines?

f. What is a palette?

g. Who is the narrator?

h. What is that turret?

 Pretend you are the girl in the portrait. It is just a day or two before you die. Write a letter to your friend in which you tell her about your horrible situation.

Say:

- Who you married
- What he is like
- What your marriage is like
- What he asked you to do
- How your husband acts now
- Why you are afraid

You can begin like this.

My dearest Constance,

I don't know if you have heard or not, but I married a short time ago.
The man I married is a ....

....

....

....

Your loving friend,

Phoebe

Who said what?

5 Below are what the characters in the story said, or what they must have said, but Edgar Allan Poe did not record for us.
Write what the characters said in the speech bubbles, and then number the pictures in the order they happened in the story.

1. Yes, if that is what you really want.
2. Why am I so fascinated by that portrait?
3. Because my husband is always away painting.
4. I must paint your portrait. Will you pose for me?
5. This is indeed Life itself!
6. Why are you so sad?
7. It is proof of both his power as a painter and of his love for his wife.
8. I am going to break into the castle because if you spend the night outside, you will die.

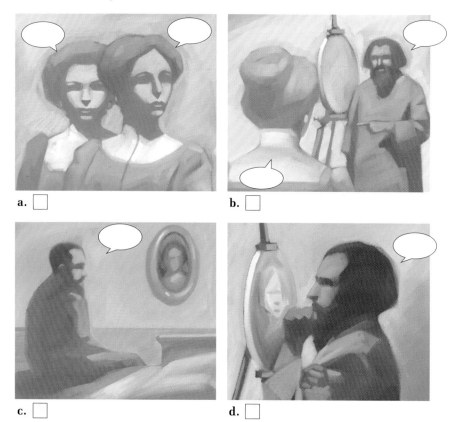

a. ☐

b. ☐

c. ☐

d. ☐

e. ☐

f. ☐

What's your opinion?

6 **Which of the following sentences do you think best sums up the story?**

☐ Art is a jealous mistress.

☐ Love hurts.

☐ Each man kills the thing he loves.

☐ Love is blind.

☐ Artists love only their art.

☐ Love is all.

☐ It is better to have loved and lost than to have never loved at all.

☐ Art is eternal, but love is not.

Compare your answers with your partner and justify your choice.

A Short History of the "Whodunit"

The detective story, also called a "whodunit" (which is a contraction of "Who has done it?" i.e., Who has done this crime?) is one of the most popular forms in all types of literature and is still very popular today. Its inventor was Edgar Allan Poe (see page 12), who also created the first important fictional detective, C. Auguste Dupin.

Sir Arthur Conan Doyle.
The National Portrait Gallery, London.

The eccentric Dupin was then the inspiration for perhaps the most famous and eccentric literary detective, and perhaps also literary character of any kind, [1] in the world, Sherlock Holmes.

Sherlock Holmes, the creation of Sir Arthur Conan Doyle (1859-1930), first appeared in a story called *A Study in Scarlet* (1887). Sherlock Holmes was a very distinctive character: he wore a strange looking

---

1. **kind** *noun* : type (**kind** as an *adjective* means *gentle, nice, friendly*).

hat called a deerstalker and a cape; [1] he also smoked a pipe and played the violin. Like Dupin he lived a solitary life and only came in contact with the outside world when he had to solve a crime.

One of the next great descendents of Poe's C. Auguste Dupin was Hercule Poirot, the creation of Dame Agatha Christie (1890-1976), who is perhaps the most popular whodunit writer in the world. The dapper [2] Hercule Poirot is also an eccentric. He is famous for his elegant looks, his slicked-down hair [3] and thin moustache and for using "little gray cells" (brain cells) to solve crimes.

Dame Agatha Christie.

Of course there are many, many other famous literary detectives in what is known as the British School of detective writing. Still, most of these detectives had something in common: most of them were amateur [4] detectives and they solved crimes for the intellectual

1. **cape :** a short coat without sleeves.
2. **dapper :** extremely elegant.
3. **slicked-down hair :** hair held down and made smooth with hair gel or cream.
4. **amateur :** not professional.

challenge; [1] in addition these detective stories were generally about the rich upper classes [2] of society and told in a refined kind of English.

In the 1920s in the United States a new kind of fictional detective was born: he was a professional detective, or private-eye, and the crimes he solved were committed in the dirty world of the big American city. These private-eyes did not speak a refined, upper-class English but a tough English full of street slang. [3] One of the most famous is Philip Marlowe, the creation of Raymond Chandler (1888-1959). Philip Marlowe is an honest, tough [4] man with no illusions living in a totally dishonest and corrupt world. He is famous for his unshaven [5] face, the ever-present Camel cigarette in his mouth and his trench coat.

Another famous American fictional detective-lawyer [6] was Perry Mason, created by Erle Stanley Gardner (1889-1970), who was himself a trial lawyer for more than 20 years. Perry Mason is perhaps the most famous lawyer in the world. He is a clean-looking professional man wearing a shirt and tie, who does his job well and always tries to help people.

But detective stories never stay the same. For example, detective stories based on real police procedures have become very popular and even science fiction (a genre Edgar Allan Poe also helped create) has been mixed with detective fiction. Monsieur Dupin's descendants will surely arrive into the 21st century.

1. **challenge** : a test of your ability to do something.
2. **upper classes** : the rich and/or the aristocracy.
3. **slang** : the informal language of a particular group, i.e., street slang, school slang.
4. **tough** [tʌf] : strong, courageous.
5. **unshaven** : his face was unshaven because he did not shave often.
6. **lawyer** [lɔːjə] : a person who has studied to work with legal matters: an advocate, a barrister.

1 Say whether the following statements are true (T) or false (F) and then correct the false ones.

		T	F
a.	Edgar Allan Poe created Sherlock Holmes.	☐	☐
b.	Sherlock Holmes is perhaps the most famous literary creation in the world.	☐	☐
c.	The detectives in many of the classic British detective stories were not professionals.	☐	☐
d.	The English in the classic British detective stories is much more formal and contains less slang than the classic American private-eye stories.	☐	☐
e.	Perry Mason created the great fictional lawyer Erle Stanley Gardner.	☐	☐
f.	Detective stories keep changing all the time and they are still very popular.	☐	☐

T: GRADE 7

2 Topic – Youth Culture
Bring a news story about a crime that has been committed by a young person recently to class. Talk about it and answer the following questions:

a. What was the crime and how do you think such a crime should be punished?

b. Why do you think the young person committed the crime?

c. What crime and detective programs are on TV in your country? Do you think they have the power to influence the behavior of young people?

3 Match the names of the famous literary detectives below with their pictures. Use the text to help you.

> Philip Marlowe   Perry Mason
> Hercule Poirot   Sherlock Holmes

THE TELL-TALE [1]
HEART

1. **tell-tale** : a tell-tale is a person who tells other people about the bad things you
   have done; (here) tell-tale is an adjective.

Before reading

1 **Parts of the human body: inside**
Look at the dictionary extracts below. Then label the parts of the human body indicated in the drawing.

blood [blʌd] *noun* : the red fluid consisting of plasma, blood cells and platelets that is pumped by the heart and carries oxygen and nutrients to all parts of the body.

bone [boʊn] *noun* : bones are the hard parts inside the body that protect organs and which form the skeleton.

brain [breɪn] *noun* : the organ within the cranium that controls thoughts, feelings and voluntary movements

heart [haːt] *noun* : **1** the muscular organ that pumps blood **2** the center of a person's emotions (especially love) **3** the center (or most important part) of something large. *The heart of the problem; the heart of the city.*

kidney [kɪdni] *noun*, **kidneys** *(plural)* : The kidneys are a pair of organs in the abdominal cavity that maintain water balance, filter blood of metabolic wastes for excretion.

liver [lɪvə] *noun* : large organ in the abdomen which purifies the blood and produces bile.

muscle [mʌsl] *noun* : a flexible tissue which can contract and relax in order to produce movement.

skull [skʌl] *noun* : the cranium.

vein [veɪn] *noun* : thin tube through which your blood flows towards your heart.

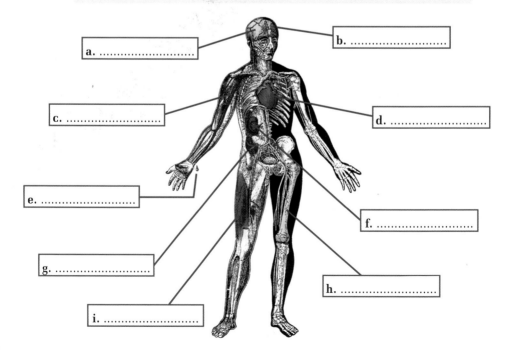

a. ....

b. ....

c. ....

d. ....

e. ....

f. ....

g. ....

h. ....

i. ....

2 The story you are going to read is about a murder. The murderer will be caught because of a *tell-tale heart*. Look at the note about *tell-tale* on page 73 and then look at the different meanings of heart on page 74.

    a. Which definition of *heart* do you think is best for the title of this story?

    ....

    ....

    ....

    b. After you have read the story, see if your answer is the same.

    ....

    ....

    ....

3 Look at the picture on page 79.
What is unusual about this old man?
What do you think of his eye?

    ☐ I find it frightening.

    ☐ It bothers me and makes me angry.

    ☐ I find it disgusting.

    ☐ It doesn't affect me at all; after all it is just a physical defect.

    ☐ Other.

FCE 4 **Listen to the first chapter of "The Tell-Tale Heart" and choose the best answer A, B or C.**

1. The narrator was, and is, very
   A ☐ angry.
   B ☐ nervous.
   C ☐ worried.

2. How did the narrator feel about the old man?
   A ☐ He loved him.
   B ☐ He hated him.
   C ☐ He was afraid of him.

3. What did the old man's eye look like?
   A ☐ It looked like a cat's eye.
   B ☐ It looked like a dog's eye.
   C ☐ It looked like a vulture's eye.

4. What did the narrator do every night around midnight?
   A ☐ He opened the door of the old man's room and then, very, very slowly, he put his head in.
   B ☐ He walked around the city, thinking up ways to kill the old man.
   C ☐ He cleaned the house.

5. What bothered the narrator?
   A ☐ The old man.
   B ☐ The old man's evil eye.
   C ☐ The old man's way of talking.

Chapter One

RUE! — nervous — very, very terribly nervous I was and I am. But why will you say that I am mad? The disease [1] made my senses extremely acute. It did not destroy them. My sense of hearing was very good. I heard all things in heaven [2] and on earth. I also heard things in hell. [3] Why, then, am I mad? Listen how healthily I can tell my story.

I cannot say how I first got the idea; but once I had it, this idea never left my brain day or night. There was no reason for this idea. There was no passion. I loved the old man. He had never done anything wrong to me. I did not want his gold. I think it was his eye! Yes, it was this! One of them looked like a vulture's [4]

1. **disease** : illness, sickness.
2. **heaven** : the place where angels and God live (heaven is up, hell is down).
3. **hell** : the place where devils and Satan live, inferno.
4. **vulture** : a large bird that eats dead animals.

eye — a pale blue eye, with a film [1] over it. When this eye looked at me, my blood became cold. And so, gradually — very gradually — I decided to kill the old man, and eliminate that eye forever.

(3)   Well, now you think I am mad. But madmen don't know anything. You should have seen me. I did everything so carefully, so intelligently. I was never kinder to the old man than during the

(4) whole [2] week before I killed him. And every night, about midnight, I opened his door slowly, very, very slowly. I opened just enough for my head. Then I put in a lantern all closed, closed so that no light came out, and then I put in my head. It was really fantastic how I did this. You would have laughed to see how slowly and intelligently I put my head in his room so that I would not wake him. It took me a whole hour to put my head into his

(5) room. Could a madman be so careful? When my head was in his room, I opened the lantern and its light fell on his vulture eye.

(6)   I did this same thing for seven nights, but each night his eye was closed, so I could not do my work. The old man did not bother [3] me. His Evil Eye bothered me.

---

1. **film** : a thin membrane or covering (oil or petrol forms a film on water).
2. **whole** [həʊl] : entire, complete.
3. **bother** : cause to be nervous, disturb.

Go back to the text

FCE 1 **Choose the correct answer A, B, C or D.**

1. Why could the narrator hear things in hell?
   - **A** ☐ Because he was mad.
   - **B** ☐ Because he was not afraid to listen.
   - **C** ☐ Because his hearing was much better than other people's.
   - **D** ☐ Because he was very nervous.

2. What happened to the narrator when he saw the old man's vulture eye?
   - **A** ☐ His blood became cold.
   - **B** ☐ He started to desire the old man's money.
   - **C** ☐ He realized how much he loved the old man.
   - **D** ☐ He realized how much he hated the old man.

3. Why did the narrator decide to kill the old man?
   - **A** ☐ Because he wanted his gold.
   - **B** ☐ Because he did not want to see the vulture eye anymore.
   - **C** ☐ Because he hated the old man.
   - **D** ☐ Because he was afraid the old man wanted to kill him.

4. According to the narrator, what do his careful preparations to kill the old man show?
   - **A** ☐ That he was not mad.
   - **B** ☐ That murder is not easy.
   - **C** ☐ That the old man was very dangerous.
   - **D** ☐ That the vulture eye was quite horrible.

5. Why couldn't the narrator "do his work" the first seven nights?
   - **A** ☐ Because the old man did not fall asleep.
   - **B** ☐ Because it took him too long to enter the old man's room.
   - **C** ☐ Because he could not see the vulture eye well enough with the lantern.
   - **D** ☐ Because the vulture eye was always closed.

How long did it take you?

Look at these questions and answers:

Q - How long does it take you to walk to school?

A - It takes me 45 minutes to walk to school.

Q - How long did it take them to get to New York?

A - It took them two hours to get to New York.

It + to take + object (noun or pronoun) + **time**
(to do something or go somewhere).

Notice that you use *how long* as the question words.

2 **Now, look at the chart and write questions and answers for each person on the chart.**

Example: *How long did it take him to tell his story?*
It took him an hour to tell his story.

	Person	Action	Lengh of Time
a.	He	put his head into the room	one hour
b.	They	find the tomb	an hour and a half
c.	The police	arrive at the scene of the crime	three hours
d.	John	drive to work	30 minutes
e.	She	get to Atlanta	eight hours

a. ....?
....

b. ....?
....

c. ....?
....

d. ....?
....

e. ....?
....

FCE 3 **Choose the most suitable heading from the list A-H for each part (1-6) of Chapter 1. There is one extra heading which you do not need to use. There is an example at the beginning (0).**

A ☐ A Horrible Defect

B ☐ A Useless Week of Waiting

C ☐ Slowly and Surely

D ☐ A Very, Very Difficult Decision

E ☐ An Innocent Victim

F ☐ There it is!

G ☐ Beyond Human Perception

H ☐ Gentle Preparations for Death

My senses were extremely acute

In English the verbs generally used with the five senses are the following:

To sound for the sense of hearing – *That music sounds horrible.*

To feel for the sense of touch – *That sweater feels soft.*

To taste for the sense of taste – *This wine tastes sweet.*

To look for the sense of sight – *He looks tired.*

To smell for the sense of smell – *Those flowers smell wonderful.*

4 **Look at the sentences below, and then complete them using the pictures opposite.**

a. He/frightened ....

b. This beer/good ....

c. That song/great ....

d. This tombstone/wet ....

e. This cheese/disgusting ....

1. ☐

2. ☐

3. ☐

4. ☐

5. ☐

5 **Read the story below and fill in the gaps with one of the five verbs from page 82.**

Herbert had prepared everything with great care. His guests would be arriving in about half and hour. He walked into the dining room. Everything (1) .... beautiful. The colorful decorations were perfect. He put his hand on the tablecloth; it (2) .... smooth and soft. Then, he tried one of the appetizers. It (3) .... delicious. Just then, though, some smoke started coming out of the kitchen. The smoke (4) .... terrible, like burnt plastic. Herbert ran into the kitchen, and opened the oven. He had forgotten to take the plastic wrapper off the chicken! Then he heard something strange under the table: it (5) .... as if an animal was chewing on something. It was an animal. It was his dog, and it was eating the birthday cake. This birthday party was not off to a good start!

Just then the phone rang.

"Hello," Herbert managed to say.

"What's wrong, Herbert?" said Julie, Herbert's girlfriend. "You (6) .... upset."

"Well," replied Herbert, "everything's wrong. I had planned everything for your party this evening, and nothing is going right."

"This evening? My party is tomorrow evening, not this evening," replied Julie.

Before reading

1 **Listen carefully!**

Below are the first four paragraphs from the second chapter of the story. They are not in the right order. Listen to the recording once and then number them in the right order. Then listen to the recording again and circle the right word to fill in the blank.

a. ☐ The *(eightieth / eighteenth / eighth)* night I was more careful than usual when I opened the door. A *(clock's / watch's / man's)* minute hand moves more quickly than my hand moved. That night I was stronger and more intelligent than I had ever been. I laughed quietly and *(possibly / maybe / perhaps)* the old man heard me because he moved.

b. ☐ I had my head in and was *(going / about / starting)* to open the lantern when the man jumped up and shouted, "*(Who's / What's / Is anybody)* there?"

c. ☐ You probably *(imagine / think / fancy)* that I pulled my head back — but no. His room was *(completely / entirely / wholly)* dark and I knew that he could not see me. I kept pushing my head in.

d. ☐ Every morning I walked *(contentedly / happily / smilingly)* into his room. I asked him if he had slept well. I talked to him like a friend. So you can see that he had to be a very *(intelligent / clever / wise)* man to suspect that every night, just at twelve, I looked at him while he *(dreamed / rested / slept)*.

Now read the chapter and check your answers.

2 **Read the passage below carefully.**
Some of the lines are correct, and some have a word which should
not be there. If a line is correct, put a tick (✓). If a line has a word
which should not be there write the word.
There are two examples at the beginning (0 and 00).

0. I did not move and said nothing. For ...✓........

00. a two whole hour I did not move a muscle and ..*two*....

1. I did not hear him lie down again. He was listening. ....

2. Then I have heard him groan, and I knew it was the groan ....

3. of mortal terror. It was not much a groan of sadness or pain ....

4. — oh no! — it comes from a horrible feeling at ....

5. the bottom of your soul. I should knew that feeling well. ....

6. I had that same feeling every night around midnight ....

7. when I wasn't looked at the old man sleeping. ....

8. I felt sorry for him, but I had to very laugh too. ....

9. His fear was growing all bigger. He tried to convince himself ....

10. that the noise came from his imagination. He said to himself, ...

11. "It is just the wind — it is only a mouse running across the floor." ....

12. Yes, he tried to comfort himself, but he found it all in vain. ....

13. All in vain, because Death's shadow already covered to the old man. ....

14. And it was Death's invisible shadow that has made him ....

15. feel the presence of my head in the room. ....

Chapter Two

very morning I walked happily into his room. I asked him if he had slept well. I talked to him like a friend. So you can see that he had to be a very wise [1] man to suspect that every night, just at twelve, I looked at him while he slept.

The eighth night I was more careful than usual when I opened the door. A watch's minute hand [2] moves more quickly than my hand moved. That night I was stronger and more intelligent than I had ever been. I laughed quietly and perhaps the old man heard me because he moved.

You probably think that I pulled my head back — but no. His room was completely dark and I knew that he could not see me. I kept pushing my head in.

---

1. **wise** : profoundly intelligent.
2. **minute hand** : a watch (clock) also has an hour hand and a second hand.

THE TELL-TALE HEART

END

I had my head in and was about to open the lantern when the man jumped up and shouted, "Who's there?"

I did not move and said nothing. For a whole hour I did not move a muscle and I did not hear him lie down again. He was listening.

Then I heard him groan, and I knew it was the groan of mortal terror. It was not a groan of sadness or pain — oh no! — it comes from a horrible feeling at the bottom of your soul. 1 I knew that feeling well. I had that same feeling every night around midnight when I looked at the old man sleeping. I felt sorry for him, but I had to laugh too.

His fear was growing bigger. He tried to convince himself that the noise came from his imagination. He said to himself, "It is just the wind — it is only a mouse running across the floor." Yes, he tried to comfort himself, but he found it all in vain. *All in vain*, because Death's shadow already covered the old man. And it was Death's invisible shadow 2 that made him *feel* the presence of my head in the room.

After I had waited for a long time, I decided to open the lantern a little tiny 3 bit. So, I opened it — you cannot imagine how carefully — until a single ray of light, like the thread 4 of a spider, 5 shot 6 out from the lantern and onto the vulture eye.

---

1. **soul** : the immortal part of a person.
2. **shadow** : area that is dark because a light source is partially blocked.
3. **tiny** : very little.
4. **thread** [θred] :
5. **spider** :
6. **shot** (shoot, shot, shot) : came out very quickly as from a pistol.

His eye was open — wide, wide open [1] — and I became furious as I looked at it. I saw it perfectly, all pale blue and with the disgusting film over it that made my bones cold; but I could see nothing else of the old man's face or body. I had, by instinct, directed the light right on that horrible spot. [2]

Now I could hear a low sound [3] like the sound of a watch enveloped [4] in cotton. I told you before I was not mad, but my senses were very acute. I knew *that* sound well too. It was the beating of the old man's heart. It made me more furious just like the beating of a drum [5] that stimulates a soldier's [6] courage.

But I did not move. I hardly breathed. [7] I held the light on the eye. And the beating of the heart increased. [8] It became quicker and quicker, and louder and louder. The old man's terror must have been extreme. It grew louder, I say, louder every moment! — do you understand? I told you I am nervous and I really am. That night that strange noise made me do something terrible.

1. **wide open** : completely open.
2. **spot** : position, place.
3. **low sound** : a sound that is difficult to hear, (for sounds **low** is the opposite of **loud**).
4. **enveloped** [ɪn'vɛləpd] : wrapped, enclosed, covered all around.
5. **drum** :
6. **soldier** [səʊldʒə] : the people who fight in armies.
7. **I hardly breathed** : I breathed just a little bit.
8. **increased** : became greater.

THE TELL-TALE HEART

The beating grew louder, louder! I thought his heart would explode. Then I thought, "Maybe the neighbors [1] will hear it!" It was the old man's moment. With a shout, I opened up the lantern completely and jumped into the room. He screamed once — once only. In an instant I pulled him to the floor and pulled the heavy bed over him. I then smiled happily because I had done so much.

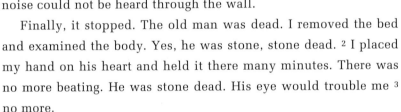

But, for many minutes, the heart continued to beat under the mattress. This, however, did not bother me: the noise could not be heard through the wall.

Finally, it stopped. The old man was dead. I removed the bed and examined the body. Yes, he was stone, stone dead. [2] I placed my hand on his heart and held it there many minutes. There was no more beating. He was stone dead. His eye would trouble me [3] no more.

1. **neighbors** [neɪbəz] : the people who live next to you are your neighbors.
2. **stone dead** : completely dead.
3. **trouble me** : bother me, give me problems.

Go back to the text

1 **Answer the following questions.**

   a. Why did the narrator talk to the old man like a friend?

   b. How many nights did the narrator watch the old man before the night he killed him?

   c. What did the narrator see when he opened the lantern?

   d. What sounded like a watch wrapped in cotton?

   e. What did the beating of the old man's heart make the narrator do?

   f. Why did the narrator think that the neighbors would hear the beating of the old man's heart?

   g. How did he kill the old man?

The old man's terror must have been extreme

Look at the following situation:
I walked past John's house last night and the light was on and I could hear music. John must have been home.

subject + must + have + past participle

John must have been home.

2 **We use this structure to draw conclusions about things that happened in the past. Draw conclusions about the sentences below. Use the phrases in the box to help you. The first has been done for you.**

> **read it**   **be a detective**   **be tired**   **know him**   **not see it**
> **break down**   **go away**   **be asleep**   **be hungry**
> **drive quickly**   **be scared**

   a. The old man screamed.
      He must have been scared.

   b. I started to tell her about the story "The Tell-Tale Heart", but she already knew how it ended.

91

c. It normally takes her three hours to drive to Baltimore but yesterday it took her only two and half hours.

d. I rang his doorbell but nobody answered the door.

e. A strange man came and started asking questions about the murder.

f. The children each ate two hamburgers and three portions of french-fries.

g. My father tripped on my brother's bicycle.

h. Edgar fell asleep at eight o'clock last night.

i. The dog did not bark when George came up to the house.

j. Allen drove to New York but he had to take a bus home again.

k. I didn't hear you open the door last night.

I hardly breathed

Look at these two sentences. Notice the position and the meaning of the adverbs *hard* and *hardly*.

*I worked **hard** = I worked with a lot of effort, force, I worked a lot.*

*I **hardly** worked = I worked very little, I scarcely worked.*

3 **Read the following sentences and then place** *hard* **or** *hardly* **in the correct position with regard to the verb in italics.**

Example: He ***hardy slept***. The sofa was very uncomfortable.

a. I .... yesterday because I was very tired. *(worked)*

b. I .... yesterday and finished all my work. *(worked)*

c. I .... I had just finished running two miles! *(breathed)*

d. I .... I did not want him to hear me. *(breathed)*

e. She .... all evening. She is a very   *(talked)*
timid person.

f. We always ...., and when we get   *(play)*
home we are very hungry.

Before reading

1 **Look at the picture on page 97.**

a. Why do you think the crazy narrator has his hands over his ears?

b. What do you think the police are thinking?

FCE **2** **Read the beginning of Chapter Three and think of the word which best fits each space. Use only one word in each space. There is an example at the beginning (0).**

If you still think (0) *that* I am mad, listen (1) ....
carefully I hid the body. The night was ending and I worked
carefully and quietly. First, I cut (2) .... the head and
the arms and the legs.

I then removed some of the boards from the floor and placed the
pieces of his body underneath. Then I put (3) .... the
boards (4) .... carefully that no human eye – not even
his – could have noticed (5) .... wrong. There was
(6) .... blood to clean – none at all – because I had been
very careful. A tub had caught (7) .... the blood –
ha! ha! ha!

(8) .... I finished my work it was four o'clock and
(9) .... was still dark. As the bell of the clock rang four
times, someone knocked (10) .... the door. I went to
open it without any fear (11) .... worry. I had nothing to
be afraid (12) ....

Then listen to the recording to check your answers.

Chapter Three

f you still think that I am mad, listen how carefully I hid the body. [1] The night was ending and I worked carefully and quietly. First, I cut off the head and the arms and the legs.

I then removed some of the boards [2] from the floor and placed the pieces of his body underneath. Then I put back the boards so carefully that no human eye — not even his — could have noticed anything wrong. There was no blood to clean — none at all — because I had been very careful. A tub [3] had caught all the blood — ha! ha! ha!

When I finished my work it was four o'clock and it was still

---

1. **hid the body** (hide, hid, hidden) : put the body in a place where nobody could find it.
2. **boards** [bɔːds] : flat pieces of wood used for construction.
3. **tub** : a large round container.

dark. As the bell of the clock rang four times, someone knocked [1] at the door. I went to open it without any fear or worry. I had

END nothing to be afraid of.

Three men came in. They introduced themselves. They were policemen. A neighbor had heard somebody scream and had thought something terrible had happened, so they called the police.

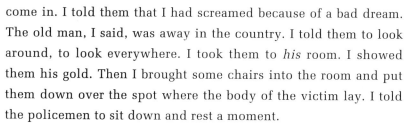

I smiled, — *what* did I have to fear? I told the policemen to come in. I told them that I had screamed because of a bad dream. The old man, I said, was away in the country. I told them to look around, to look everywhere. I took them to *his* room. I showed them his gold. Then I brought some chairs into the room and put them down over the spot where the body of the victim lay. I told the policemen to sit down and rest a moment.

The policemen were satisfied. I had convinced them. They sat and I talked happily. But, in a few moments, I felt myself getting pale and I wanted them to go. My head ached [2] and I heard a ringing [3] in my ears. But they continued to talk. The ringing became more distinct: I talked more and more to try to eliminate the feeling. Then I discovered that the noise was not in my ears.

---

1. **knocked** : hit the door with fist (closed hand) so that the person inside would open it.
2. **ached** [eɪkd] : (here) hurt.
3. **ringing** : the sound a bell makes.

I became very pale and I talked louder and louder. But the sound increased — and what could I do? It was a low sound — *very much like a watch enveloped in cotton*. I could hardly breathe, but the policemen could not hear the sound. I talked more quickly. I talked more loudly, but the noise increased. I stood up and began to argue [1] about stupid things. I shouted, I moved my arms about. Why didn't those policemen leave? I walked around the room quickly — but the noise still increased. Oh God! What could I do? I screamed, I shouted! I pulled the chair over the place where the noise came from, but the noise was still louder, louder — *louder*! And still the men talked happily and smiled.

Didn't they hear? Oh God! No, no! They heard! — they suspected! — they *knew*! — they were making fun of [2] my horror! This I thought and this I think. But anything was better than this agony, than their making fun of me! I could not bear [3] their hypocritical smiles any more. I felt that I must scream or die! — and now again! — Listen! Louder! Louder! Louder! *Louder*! —

"Villains!" [4] I screamed, "do not pretend [5] any more! I admit what I did! — Pull up the boards! — Here! here! It is the beating of his hideous [6] heart!"

---

1. **argue** : discuss aggressively in order to convince someone.
2. **making fun of** : not taking it seriously (they thought his horror was something funny).
3. **I could not bear** : I could not tolerate = I could not stand.
4. **Villains** : Terrible people, criminals.
5. **do not pretend** : this means, do not act as if you *can't* hear the beating of his heart, because I know that you really *can* hear it.
6. **hideous** : horrible, awful.

Go back to the text

1 **Answer the following questions.**

  a. Where did the crazy narrator hide the body?

  ....

  b. When did he finish hiding it?

  ....

  c. Who knocked at the door then?

  ....

  d. Why wasn't he afraid?

  ....

  e. Why had the police come to the house?

  ....

  f. How did the crazy narrator convince them that nothing was wrong?

  ....

  g. What did the crazy narrator begin to hear?

  ....

  h. What did he do to hide the noise?

  ....

  i. How did the policemen discover the body?

  ....

A mad point of view

2 **The sentences in column A are the narrator's explanations for what happens in the story. Match these sentences with the explanations in column B, which are more probable and, perhaps, more logical.**

A

1. The narrator did not become mad: he had a disease that made him hear better than most people.
2. It was very intelligent how the narrator planned and executed the murder of the old man.
3. The old man's vulture eye was a kind of evil spirit that was always looking at the narrator.
4. The real, physical beating heart of the old man was the tell-tale.
5. The police smiled at the narrator because they wanted to make fun of him.
6. The noise of the beating heart became louder and louder.

B

a. The narrator only thought he heard a beating heart.
b. The police smiled uncomfortably at the narrator because they were shocked by his strange actions.
c. The narrator's conscious (or perhaps the spirit of the perverse) made him show the police where the body was hidden not the sound of a beating heart.
d. The old man's vulture eye was a normal physical defect.
e. There was no reason to put his head so slowly into the old man's room for seven nights.
f. A disease made the narrator mad.

Summary

 3 **Below is a summary of "The Tell-Tale Heart". Five paragraphs have been removed. Choose the best paragraph from the list A-F for each part 1-4. There is one extra paragraph which you do not need to use. The first one has been done for you.**

This is the story of a man who is totally mad. He says that he isn't but we are quite certain that he is. He tells the story of why and how he killed an old man.

0 | D

This eye bothered him so much that he decided to kill the old man and to eliminate the eye forever. Each night for seven nights he opened the door of the old man's room and put his head in very slowly, but the eye was always closed.

1

Then the crazy narrator says that he heard a sound like a watch enveloped in cotton. This was the old man's heart. This sound grew so loud that the narrator was afraid that the neighbors would hear it.

2

He then cut up the old man's body and hid it under the boards of the floor. He was certain that no one would ever find it.

3

Then he asked them to sit on some chairs which were directly over the cut-up parts of the old man's body. At first the narrator felt good, but then he became pale and his head ached.

4

He thought they were making fun of his horror. Finally he could not stand it any more and he told them to pull up the boards to see the hideous beating heart.

A   On the eighth night, he made some noise and the old man woke up and said, "Who's there?" After a few minutes the old man screamed because he was afraid.

B   For seven days he heard the sound of the old man's heart. It was so horrible for him that he finally decided to kill the old man, and that is what he did on the eighth night.

C   At four o'clock someone knocked at the door. It was the police. A neighbor had heard someone scream. He told them that he had had a bad dream and that the old man was in the country. He also showed them the old man's gold.

D   He is not sure how he first got this idea: he loved the old man and he did not want his gold. In any case, the old man had a strange pale blue eye with a film over it. It looked like the eye of a vulture.

E   Then he started to hear the beating of the old man's heart. It got louder and louder. He was sure that they could hear it too, but they just smiled at him.

F   Finally he jumped into the room, and pulled a bed over the old man. After some time the noise stopped. He examined the body and the old man was stone dead.

Two Kings of Hollywood Horror
Roger Corman and Vincent Price

Edgar Allan Poe has had an important influence on Hollywood. The ideas from his stories have been used in many films, in particular in the films of Roger Corman (1926-). Roger is one of the most successful independent directors [1] in film history. He is particularly famous for the low cost of his films and the very short time he took in making them (sometimes less than two weeks). He

Vincent Price in a scene of *The Fly* (1958).

kept the costs low by using unknown actors and often reusing the sets of other films. Roger also added humor to standard Hollywood genres like the horror movie.

Finally Roger is famous for helping many young people begin their careers in films. Some of the most famous examples are the directors Francis Ford Coppola, Peter Bogdanovich, Martin Scorsese, and the actors Jack Nicholson, Robert De Niro and Charles Bronson.

---

1. **directors** : people who manage (direct) the making of a film.

However, the actor most closely associated with Roger's Poe films is Vincent Price (1911-1993). The two of them made four films based on Poe stories: *The Pit and the Pendulum*, 1961, *Tales of Terror*, 1962, *The Raven*, 1963, *Masque of the Red Death*, 1964. They are now considered classics.

Vincent was a very cultured and sophisticated actor, but he is most famous for his horror movies, such as the four Poe movies mentioned above, as well as *House of Wax* (1953), *The Fly* (1958). *The Abominable Dr. Phibes* (1971) *Theatre of Blood* (1973). Vincent acted until the end of his life, and his last important role was as the kind, old creator of Edward in the film *Edward Scissorhands* (1990). Vincent had a good sense of humor as can be heard in his rap narration of Michael Jackson's video and song "Thriller".

Vincent Price in a scene of *Masque of the Red Death* (1964).

1 Say whether the following sentences are true (T) or false (F) and then correct the false ones.

		T	F
a.	Roger Corman's films took a long time to make and they were always very expensive.	☐	☐
b.	Martin Scorsese is a famous actor.	☐	☐
c.	Charles Bronson is a famous director.	☐	☐
d.	Vincent Price acted in the movie *Edward Scissorhands* when he was a very young man.	☐	☐
e.	Roger Corman did a rap song with Michael Jackson.	☐	☐
f.	The Poe movies that Roger and Vincent made are still considered great movies today.	☐	☐

INTERNET PROJECT

Use one of the principal search engines to find out about Edgar Allan Poe's different houses. See if you can find out the following:

- Where they are located.
- Which of his famous stories he wrote in them.
- What they are used for today.
- When and how to visit them.

A Mysterious Death

Till this day nobody knows exactly how Edgar Allan Poe died. In fact, there are many theories and legends which surround his death. Use the Internet to find three of them and say:

- Which one you think is most plausible.
- Which one you think is most intriguing.
- Which one you think is most absurd.

FCE **1** **The Black Cat. Choose the best answer A, B, C or D.**

1. As a child, the narrator particularly liked

   A ☐ taking long walks in the countryside.

   B ☐ hurting black cats.

   C ☐ animals.

   D ☐ fishing.

2. The narrator's wife said that Pluto was a witch in disguise because

   A ☐ it had only one eye.

   B ☐ it had a white spot that looked like a gallows.

   C ☐ it was black, large and very intelligent.

   D ☐ it followed them everywhere.

3. The narrator's personality changed because

   A ☐ he began to drink.

   B ☐ he was bitten by his cat.

   C ☐ his house and all his wealth were destroyed in a fire.

   D ☐ he became terrified of ending up on the gallows for his crime.

4. Perverseness is when

   A ☐ you do something evil.

   B ☐ you hurt someone you love.

   C ☐ you do something only because you know you shouldn't do it.

   D ☐ you do something only because you know you should do it.

5. The narrator tells about the fire that destroyed his house because

   A ☐ he wants to record the facts of his story and nothing more.

   B ☐ he saw it as divine punishment for having killed Pluto.

   C ☐ he wants people to know about it and feel sorry for him.

   D ☐ he sees it as proof of his idea of "perverseness".

6. At first the narrator did not hurt his second black cat because

   A ☐ it looked so much like Pluto.

   B ☐ he was too ashamed.

   C ☐ it was so affectionate.

   D ☐ it had a spot that looked like the gallows.

7. The narrator felt happy and peaceful after he had killed his wife because

   A ☐   she would no longer protect the black cat.

   B ☐   the black ran away and he did not see it anymore.

   C ☐   he liked being perverse.

   D ☐   he could now live alone with the black cat.

8. How did the police finally discover the corpse of the narrator's wife?

   A ☐   The cat began crying behind the wall.

   B ☐   The cat walked over to the place where his wife was hidden and began to cry.

   C ☐   They saw the blood on the ground near the wall.

   D ☐   The narrator pointed to the place where she was hidden with the cane.

FCE 2 **The Oval Portrait. Choose the best answer A, B, C or D.**

1. Pedro took the narrator into the abandoned castle because

   A ☐   the narrator had been hurt and had a fever.

   B ☐   he knew that the narrator was interested in art.

   C ☐   he knew that the narrator was interested in ghosts.

   D ☐   they were both tired and wished to sleep indoors.

2. The narrator was moved by the portrait because

   A ☐   it was so well done that the girl looked real.

   B ☐   the expression on the girl's face looked so real.

   C ☐   it was hidden in a niche and could only be seen with the light of the candelabrum.

   D ☐   the girl in the picture had died for love.

3. While painting his wife, the painter became obsessed with

   A ☐   capturing every color of life on her face.

   B ☐   her great beauty.

   C ☐   the strange expression on her face.

   D ☐   the fact that she was becoming more and more ill.

4. People who saw the artist working thought that the painting showed

   A ☐ how cruel the painter was.

   B ☐ how much he loved his wife and how great a painter he was.

   C ☐ an incredible lifelikeness.

   D ☐ that he only cared about his art.

5. The artist trembled when he finished the painting because

   A ☐ his wife died in that same moment.

   B ☐ it was the best painting he had ever done.

   C ☐ it seemed to be life itself.

   D ☐ it was even more beautiful than his wife.

FCE 3 **The Tell-Tale Heart. Choose the best answer A, B, C or D.**

1. The narrator says that the disease

   A ☐ made him kill the old man.

   B ☐ made his sense of hearing extremely good.

   C ☐ made him want to have the old man's gold.

   D ☐ love the old man.

2. According to the narrator, the careful and intelligent way in which he prepared to kill the old man shows that

   A ☐ he wasn't mad.

   B ☐ he was very nervous.

   C ☐ he was mad.

   D ☐ he should not have been arrested by the police.

3. The narrator decided it was the moment to kill the old man because

   A ☐ the light of the lantern fell on the vulture eye.

   B ☐ the beating of the old man's heart was making him nervous.

   C ☐ he was afraid that the neighbors would hear the old man scream.

   D ☐ he was afraid that the neighbors would hear the beating of the old man's heart.

4. The narrator was not afraid when the policemen arrived at his house because

A ☐ he had hid the cut-up body so well.

B ☐ nobody had seen him kill the old man.

C ☐ the old man's heart had stopped beating.

D ☐ the old man's gold was still in the house.

5. When the policemen smiled at him the narrator thought

A ☐ they knew that he had killed the old man.

B ☐ they were making fun of him because he was so terrified.

C ☐ they did not think that he killed the old man.

D ☐ they were making fun of him because he had had a bad dream.

FCE 4 **The Police Report**

Pretend that you are one of the policeman who visited the house of the narrator of "The Tell-Tale Heart". Write a report on what happened. Include the following information:

- Why you went to his house
- How he acted at first
- How he began to act
- What your feelings were
- How you discovered the cut-up body

5 **The Logic of Horror**

Edgar Allan Poe was greatly interested in logic: he wrote about thinking machines, secret codes and scientific detection. So, it is no coincidence that his tales of horror do not depend on supernatural phenomena such as ghosts and demons, but on the bizarre logic that dominates sick minds; this is in the end much more frightening than any monster or ghost: after all, we cannot escape our own minds!

a. How is the narrator of "The Black Cat" logical?

b. How is the narrator of "The Tell-Tale Heart" logical?

6 **The Spirit of Perverseness**

   a. What is the spirit of perverseness?

   b. How is this spirit a key "character" in both "The Black Cat" and "The Tell-Tale Heart"?

7 **Two Parallel Tales**

   a. How are "The Black Cat" and "The Tell-Tale Heart" similar?

8 **The Lifelikeness of her Expression**
In "The Oval Portrait" the narrator tells us that a painting woke him from his stupor. However, it was not the lifelikeness of the painting in general, but the lifelikeness of the expression which moved him.

   a. What do you think the expression of the girl communicated to the narrator?

   b. What do the narrator and the girl in the painting have in common?

9 **Sight and Sound**

   a. How is sound important in "The Black Cat"? In "The Tell-Tale Heart"?

   b. How is sight important in "The Black Cat"? In "The Oval Portrait" ? In "The Tell-Tale Heart"?

10 **Obsessed**
As we noted above, the characters of Poe's tales of horror are not possessed by supernatural beings. But they are possessed by obsessions! What are the obsessions of the:

- Narrator of "The Black Cat"?
- Narrator of "The Tell-Tale Heart"?
- The painter in "The Oval Portrait"?

FCE 11 Of which of the people A-D are the following true?

A The narrator of "The Black Cat".

B The narrator of "The Oval Portrait".

C The painter in "The Oval Portrait".

D The narrator of "The Tell-Tale Heart".

0 He was obsessed with capturing life. C

1 He was a victim of alcohol.

2 He loved animals as a child.

3 He planned what he thought was the perfect murder.

4 His obsession made him let his wife die.

5 His killed his wife out of pure anger.

6 He killed because he knew that God would not forgive him.

7 He could not see what was happening in front of him.

8 He was the victim of his hate for a physical defect.

9 He told his tale the day before his death.

10 He was charmed by the face of a dying girl.

11 He lost all his possessions in a fire.

12 He did not steal his victim's gold.

13 He put this hand on a beating heart.

14 He married when he was a young man.

15 First, he was obsessed with the sight of his victim and then he was obsessed by the sound of his victim.

policemen sit down over the cut-up body.

7 In both tales the narrators do horrible actions because of some physical problem: one drinks too much and the other has some terrible disease. And yet both narrators explain their crimes as if some horrible outside agent had caused them to kill: the spirit of the perverse, for the first, and excited senses for the second. Both narrators explain carefully their actions, and neither one really accepts any supernatural explanation for his actions or the things that happen. The first narrator mentions in passing that his wife thought that Pluto was a witch in disguise and that there was the image of a cat on the wall. The second narrator never even bothers to think about how the heart of a dead man could continue beating; for him his over acute sense of hearing explains everything.

8
a. Perhaps a sense of fear and desperation.
b. They were both in the same room and they were both "captured" by art. Also, they were both ill and suffering. Perhaps the narrator saw his own fear of death in the young girl's face.

9
a. In "The Black Cat" the narrator and the police hear the screaming of the cat and so the wife's corpse is discovered. In "The Tell-Tale Heart" the narrator is excited to murder because he hears the beating heart, and then he reveals the cut-up body of the murdered man because he "hears" the beating heart.
b. In "The Black Cat" the narrator sees the image of the hanged cat, and, more important, he thinks he can see the gallows in the spot on the cat, or in other words, he can see he his own horrible fate. In "The Oval Portrait" the narrator is wakened from his stupor by the sight of the portrait. Then, of course, the painter looks at his wife and sees every detail of her face, without, though, "seeing" that she is dying. In "The Tell-Tale Heart" the narrator kills because he cannot stand the sight of the old man's eye.

10 The narrator of "The Black Cat" is obsessed by the black cats. He never says that he believes the two cats are evil, but both of them cause him to do evil things: the first one, Pluto, because it is so good and loves him; and the second one because its white spot seems to him to predict his own death by hanging.
The narrator of "The Tell-Tale Heart" is obsessed by his own senses, and by the horrible blue eye.
The painter in "The Oval Portrait" is obsessed with "capturing" life in a painting.

11 1. A, 2. A, 3. D, 4. C, 5. A, 6. A, 7. C, 8. D, 9. A, 10. B, 11. A, 12. D, 13. D, 14. A, 15. D

Exit Test Answer Key

1 1. C, 2. C, 3. A, 4. C, 5. A, 6. D,
7. B, 8. A

2 1. A, 2. B, 3. A, 4. B, 5. C

3 1. B, 2. A, 3. D, 4. A, 5. B

4 Two other police officers and myself were called to 101 Maple Lane because a neighbor had heard a horrible scream. We knocked at the door and a young man opened. He acted quite normally, and explained to us that he had had a terrible nightmare. This he said was the reason for the scream. He also told us calmly about the owner of the house, who he said was in the country. Everything seemed in order and we were about to leave. Then the young man asked us to sit and rest for a moment. We began talking and then he began to get slightly upset. At first he only smiled nervously and we smiled back nervously. Then he began to talk rapidly and loudly. Of course, we began to suspect something, but we did nothing. Still, his nervousness increased and finally he shouted out that we must pull up the floor boards (At this point I believe he said something about a "hideous heart"). We then pulled up the boards and found the body of Mr .... which the young man had cut up into numerous pieces.

5 **a.** He tells us his story calmly. He explains the reason for each of his actions: he was a gentle boy so he loved animals; he began to drink and his mood changed; he killed Pluto because he was dominated by the Spirit of the Perverse; there was an image on the wall of the house because of a chemical reaction; and his fear of the second cat was due to its strange resemblance to Pluto and a spot on its breast resembling the gallows.

b. This narrator begins his story by explaining why he was capable of hearing so well. He said he had a disease which made his hearing more acute. This is why he could hear the old man's heart, both when he was about to kill him and when the heart "was beating" under the floor.
Second, he analyzes logically his reason for killing the old man: it was not for money; it was not because he hated him; it was because he could not stand his horrible eye.

6 **a.** This is the spirit that makes you do things which you know are wrong because you know they are wrong.

b. The narrator of "The Black Cat" kills Pluto under the influence of this "character", and then this "character" causes him to hit the wall with his cane.
In "The Tell-Tale Heart" this spirit (or a very similar one!) causes the narrator to kill an old man whom he loved just because the old man has a horrible eye like a vulture. Then, the narrator, for no particularly reason, has the